£12.00

Computing Shape

D1556019

This book is to be returned on or before
the last date stamped below.

?

Computing Shape

An introduction to the representation of component and assembly
geometry for computer-aided engineering

John Woodwark

IBM UK Scientific Centre, Winchester

Butterworths
London Boston Durban Singapore Sydney Toronto Wellington

First published 1986

© J R Woodwark, 1986

British Library Cataloguing in Publication Data

Woodwark, John
    Computing shape: an introduction to the representation of component and assembly geometry for computer-aided engineering
    1. Engineering design — Data processing
    I. Title
    620′.00425′0285   TA174
    ISBN 0–408–01402–4

Library of Congress Cataloging in Publication Data

Woodwark, John.
    Computing shape.

    Bibliography: p.
    Includes index.
    1. Engineering design—Data processing.
    2. Computer-aided design.   I. Title.
    TA174.W59   1986   620′.00425′0285   85-31328
    ISBN 0–408–01402–4

Typeset by Scribe Design, Gillingham, Kent
Printed and bound in England by Butler & Tanner, Frome, Somerset

Preface

There is no lack of articles in the technical press on the applications of computers to engineering design and manufacture. Even the newspapers are not averse to telling us what industrial robots can and cannot do, or alternatively what other countries have, and ours hasn't, done. (This probably applies whatever the nationality of the reader.) Recently, a few books have appeared that deal with computers applied to engineering in general. At a much greater level of detail is a large technical literature which it is not easy to enter except, perhaps, via infrequent review papers. In this book I have sought to take a middle way and to discuss one of the major components of this new technology at a level between the catch-all book, where it might comprise half a chapter, and technical papers, where it might occupy a dozen box files. The reader may use the book to make the jump into the literature, and a selection of the references at the end are asterisked for that purpose.

Parts of the book are loosely based on two sets of notes that were first issued to people from industry on short courses, and subsequently used as final-year undergraduate lecture notes. The intended readership has not changed. The student market is popular with my publishers, but I would also like to reach people working in the engineering industry. In particular I would like to think that engineers facing the baying of the software salesmen, or whose jobs have suddenly acquired an unwelcome computing element, will find it useful.

Even the general reader may find this book stimulating and, having read it, will have the pleasure of reading some of the more technical articles in the newspapers with a superior air.

Media interest in 'information technology' has not been entirely divorced from perceptions of its possible effects on the jobs people do, and perhaps eventually on the whole idea of work. In the case of computers in engineering, this is added to the 'tanks or tractors' dichotomy that has always been present in engineering. To say that I would not myself like to do some of the tasks that have been brought to my attention as candidates for automation is a considerable understatement. Those of my readers who have started work in a foundry, say, early on a dark winter's morning, will understand my thoughts. I only hope that their stay was as short as mine.

In the end, it is to be hoped that the decision to adopt new technologies will be a consensus of some kind. Whether human labour that is remitted in the process is labelled as 'leisure', or 'unemployment', is a political question. I see no reason why those of us who are involved in developing new technology should have any more say than anyone else. What we do have is a duty to see that people know what is on offer and understand that magic is not involved. In a small way I hope that this book discharges some obligations in that respect.

A book about shape would make little sense without pictures. In addition to providing explanatory diagrams I have included what I hope are understandable examples of the things that actual computer programs can achieve. I would like to thank the people who provided me with output that I could not otherwise have obtained. I am grateful both for their time (a number of people prepared pictures specially) and also for acceding to my request for simplicity. All the systems illustrated are capable of much more than these figures show, but I asked for, and got, pictures that would be comprehensible when reduced to the size of these pages. The contributors were: Tony Billett, Maurice Bonney, Ian Braid, Adrian Geisow, Ed Lambourne, John Manning, Brian Nightingale, Sue Toyne, Andy Wallis, Andrew Whitten and Laurence Wickens. Credits to organizations are given with the figure captions. The computer-generated figures without an acknowledgement were produced by myself or my colleagues at the University of Bath or, earlier, at the University of Leeds. I would like to express my appreciation of the facilities made available to me by these institutions.

The text of this book has been vastly improved by suggestions from people, with very different interests in the subject, whom I managed to persuade to read it in draft. I would like to thank Adrian Geisow, Stephen Hunter, Jonathan Knight, Ed Lambourne, Kevin Quinlan, Stephen Spooner and Phil Willis. I am especially grateful to three further people who have exceeded any reasonable expectations I might have had of them: Adrian Bowyer and Malcolm Sabin, who both made a large number of valuable comments, and agreed to a further reading after I had made changes, and my wife Flavia, who did a great deal of the typing, had several purges on my English, spelling and punctuation, and smiled (in a wintry way) at missed deadlines. The errors and obscurities that remain in this book will surely be in the places where I ignored the advice I was offered.

J.R.W.

Contents

1

Introduction

This book is an introduction to one of the component technologies of *computer-aided engineering*. The phrase is a piece of jargon that refers to the applications of computers to engineering in general. By abbreviating it to CAE, the author is following common practice, and possibly saving a small tree. CAE encompasses both of the older terms *computer-aided design* (CAD) and *computer-aided manufacture* (CAM), which in any case overlap considerably.

The range of processes that can be grouped under the heading CAE is enormous. Examples are design automation, numerically controlled machining, industrial robotics and flexible manufacturing systems. The interpretation of CAE, and the processes that are actually computerized, vary between the different engineering disciplines. In this book we will be discussing techniques that apply most directly to the geometry or shape of *mechanical* components and assemblies. This topic is primarily of interest to mechanical engineers but, although they may bewail the fact, engineers of all specializations need to deal with the spatial problems involved in putting together the things that they design.

A mechanical component or assembly may be anything from a washer to an airframe. However simple or complex, mechanical components must generally be designed, manufactured, tested and assembled. There are CAE techniques to help with all of these processes, and if the component is the airframe we shall

certainly need them. In the case of the washer the only computer assistance that may be required is to know how many there are in the stores. If that is absolutely all that is necessary then the reader should consult a book on databases[20]. As soon as we want the washer to appear on a drawing, or to be picked up by a robot, then its *shape* becomes important. If a computer is going to help in doing these things it must 'know' something about the shape: there must be a shape representation somewhere within its program. Many people have written programs that do useful things with simple shapes like washers without realizing that they were incorporating some information about the shape of a washer, or washers in general, into their computer code. This is a pity, because then they cannot easily extend their program, nor use the shape representation in another program. As well as *data* about shape, programs also contain *algorithms*, or procedures, that are able to make use of the shape information. In this book the intention is to differentiate clearly between the ways in which shape information is represented and the ways in which it is used. Whether we try to disguise it or not, shape representations will remain fundamental in applying computer-based techniques to mechanical engineering, and hence to an important part of all engineering activities.

If we only want to make washers things are straightforward: only three numbers are required to specify the dimensions of a plain

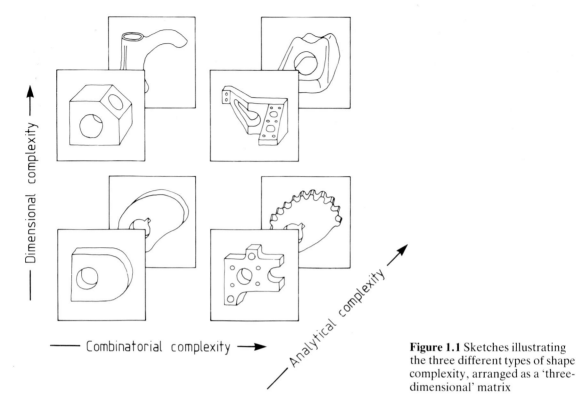

Figure 1.1 Sketches illustrating the three different types of shape complexity, arranged as a 'three-dimensional' matrix

washer (to pursue the matter of washers, see Figure 7.13). Of course, mechanical components are generally much more complex. It is possible to distinguish between three different types of complexity that are all present in varying degrees in a given object (Figure 1.1).

(1) *Combinatorial complexity*
An object may be complex because of the sheer number of shape elements that are present, even if they are individually as simple to describe as a washer. If there are n shape elements, there are $\frac{1}{2}n(n - 1)$ pairs of elements which may interact in various ways.

(2) *Dimensional complexity*
Even if an object only incorporates simple shape features, these may be more or less difficult to deal with depending on the range of orientations that they are able to assume. If we know that an object is basically two-dimensional there are many short cuts that can be taken. Unlike combinatorial complexity, there is a limit to the dimensional complexity of objects when their shape elements are allowed to occupy any position or orientation in space. (Although trajectories of moving objects offer a further set of problems.)

(3) *Analytical complexity*
The algebra of the individual shape elements which make up an object may also be simple or complex. If the shape elements have flat surfaces and straight edges then they are going to be easier to deal with than curves and curved surfaces. Singly curved surfaces like cylinders and cones are in turn simpler than doubly curved, twisted forms.

The remainder of this book is intended to follow in order of increasing complexity. As we have just shown that shape complexity may be considered as a three-dimensional quantity, our ordering must be approximate. Each chapter describes a class of representations and some of the algorithms that have been developed to use them. Not only do the nature and objectives of each class of representation differ, but so does the relative sophistication of a representation itself as against the algorithms that deal with it. The face models of Chapter 5, for instance, are very simple to describe, but the computer graphics community has put a lot of work into developing ways of producing very realistic pictures from them. While on this subject, the reader will soon notice the disproportionate amount of space allocated to describing algorithms for generating pictures as against other CAE processes. This weighting simply reflects the balance of achievements to date. In any case, some pictorial output is a first and essential process in most shape computations, so we can check that the computer is working with the correct geometry. However, it is also true that many techniques first used in making pictures have subsequently found other applications.

2

Two-dimensional geometry and drawings

In this chapter we shall start to look at what can be done in a computer using only two-dimensional geometry. The problems encountered in computerizing geometric constructions that schoolchildren can do without difficulty may surprise the reader, but the difficulties that occur in three dimensions are even greater. In some cases, procedures only exist for the two-dimensional version of a computation. Because of this relative simplicity, and because of the two-dimensional nature of paper and television-type screens, it is prudent to remain in two dimensions for as long as possible.

The first application of computerized two-dimensional geometry that we shall examine is automating the production of engineering drawings. As we shall see, this is far from synonymous with constructing representations of shape which are useful *inside* a computer. However, the production of drawings using a computer is a large part of CAE in commercial terms, as companies naturally seek compromises with existing patterns of work. Examining the bases of systems which produce drawings also provides an introduction to some of the ideas that will be explored further in succeeding chapters.

Putting two-dimensional geometry into the computer

Before looking at any systems, we shall see how some very simple geometric data may be represented and manipulated in a computer. (The author deals with this topic in more detail in ref. 11.) In addition to the points, lines and circles discussed below we may also wish to use curves of the sort that a draughtsman would use a French curve to draw. These are discussed separately in the next chapter.

Points

All the geometry we are going to talk about in this book uses the Cartesian system. Points are defined by x and y coordinates. Perhaps the simplest geometric structure that we can think of is a number of points in a plane (meaning, on a flat surface). Points are likely to be only part of the data in an engineering application, but they might do very well on their own for, say, a botanist who wished to record the positions of specimens of a particular plant growing in a field. Supposing our botanist only wants to add points to, and to delete points from, a list stored in a computer. Imagine also that these points are pictured as flower symbols, as in Figure 2.1.

Adding more flowers is really very easy. The botanist specifies a pair of position coordinates (x, y) to the program maintaining his data. The computer creates a record of the new flower's position and adds it to the list, whose length increases by one. The only difficulty arises when the computer storage assigned to the list is exhausted, when the new flower must (with regret) be rejected.

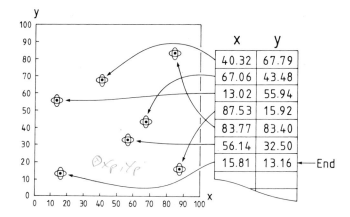

x	y
40.32	67.79
67.06	43.48
13.02	55.94
87.53	15.92
83.77	83.40
56.14	32.50
15.81	13.16

←End

Figure 2.1 A list of point coordinate values drawn as 'flower' symbols

Deletion is a much more difficult problem. First, the botanist must indicate in some way the flower that he wants removed from the list. It would not be convenient for him to have to remember every decimal point of every flower's coordinates. If he has a map of where the flowers are (either on a piece of paper or on some television-like device connected to a computer), then he can point to the flower to be deleted. In effect, the botanist specifies a pair of coordinates near to the flower he wants to get rid of, and a program looks down the list to find the flower nearest to the specified position. This can be done by calculating the distance from the point specified to every flower in turn using Pythagoras' theorem:

$$s = \sqrt{[(x_F - x_P)^2 + (y_F - y_P)^2]} \quad \text{HYPOTENUSE}$$

where (x_F, y_F) is the position of a flower, and (x_P, y_P) is the position the botanist specified. The smallest distance (value of s) corresponds to the nearest flower, which is thus selected for deletion.

There are important efficiency considerations here. The square root function is slow on most computers, and here we are planning to use it once for every record in what might be a long list. An immediate improvement can be made by omitting the square root operation and comparing squared distances (s^2) instead. The minimum squared distance will still correspond to the same flower. We can also avoid some of the multiplications involved in taking squares by calculating both $(x_F - x_P)$ and $(y_F - y_P)$ before squaring either. Whichever expression has the largest absolute value is squared first; if it is larger than the smallest s^2 found so far, the second square need not be calculated at all. Alternatively, a value of the smallest s may be maintained (but this reintroduces the need for some square roots) and compared directly with the absolute values, or moduli, $|x_F - x_P|$ and $|y_F - y_P|$.

Even with these refinements, if the list of flowers is very long it will be time-consuming just to consult every record. To get around this problem the point data may be structured so that a point can be accessed by reference to a region in which it resides. This is not unlike the arrangement used in street maps, where an index of street names refers the reader to the square or squares of a grid in which the street lies (Figure 2.2). Like the reader of a street map, a computer can find data much faster if it is organized on a *spatially referenced* basis than if it has to search through every data item. An alternative to a regular grid is a spatial division based on what is called a *tree* structure: so called because diagrammatically it looks like a tree, but upside down. Each *node*, or element, of the tree may either contain data, when it is called a *leaf*, or it may *branch* and point to two or more nodes below. In the present case (Figure 2.3), every branching of the tree corresponds to a division of the area, and leaf nodes contain the point data. A tree structure uses storage much more efficiently than a grid when data are unevenly spaced, although access is not quite so quick.

When it has at last been decided which point is to be deleted, our problems are not over. Getting rid of a point will cause a 'hole' in the

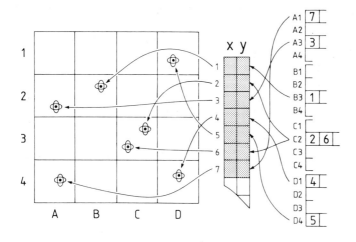

Figure 2.2 Points stored for access using a grid. There is a list of point numbers corresponding to each square on the grid. Each point number provides an index into a list of coordinate values

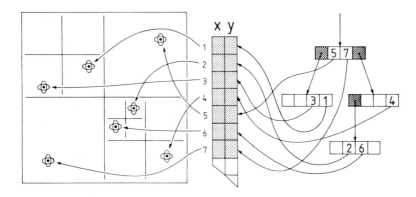

Figure 2.3 Points stored for access using a tree structure. A node in the tree may point to nodes below (corresponding to a division of the area), be an index into a list of coordinate values, or be null (corresponding to an empty sub-area)

data structure. If it is a simple list all the points can be shuffled up, but this is slow if the list is a long one. Alternatively a deletion marker can be attached to the unwanted point. This may be a large value in the place of, say, the x coordinate: too large to represent a point in the field. (Zero cannot normally be used, of course: that describes a point on the y axis.) Alternatively, each point record could have space for a separate deletion marker. After a lot of deletions have occurred, a shuffle may be necessary to save space, and also to reduce the amount of time wasted examining deleted points. With the more sophisticated spatially referenced data structures of Figures 2.2 and 2.3, it would not be usual to move the point coordinate data around. Instead we introduce pointers to the coordinate values, and changes are reflected by modifications to these. Additional structures are then required to keep

track of the storage freed. Programs using data arranged in this way must be reliable. One incorrect pointer in tens of thousands of data items can cause the whole edifice to collapse.

We have pursued this subject of points in a plane in some detail to show that there may be subtleties in the computerization of a task that can be done by hand by pencilling a few crosses on a piece of paper, with a rubber as a delete function. The advantages of the computer system—speed, accuracy, and data capacity—are not obtained without some effort, and there are inherent limits to even the computer's performance on these problems.[62] This simple example should have shown that, even when geometric structures and efficient procedures have been determined, there is a further level of organization required to implement an actual computer system. These levels are never wholly distinct but to the extent that they are, this book concentrates on the higher level, geometric, activities. Page and Wilson[52] provide an admirable introduction to the techniques of data structuring *per se*, and Day[19] presents similar material in the context of the FORTRAN language, still ubiquitous in CAE applications.

Straight lines

Most readers will recognize the equation

$$y = mx + c$$

as that of a straight line in Cartesian coordinates. The constant m is the line's gradient and c is its intercept with the y axis, as shown in Figure 2.4. Points on the line may be generated

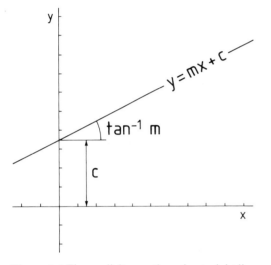

Figure 2.4 The explicit equation of a straight line

by deciding on a value of x and inserting it into the right-hand side of the equation, which yields the corresponding value of y. This *explicit* equation unfortunately breaks down when lines become near to vertical. In this case the value of m tends towards infinity. The human geometer knows to use the alternative form

$$x = k$$

for a vertical line, but this is very inconvenient in a computer program. Not only must every algorithm be written in two versions, one for vertical lines and one for others, but the large values of m which correspond to near-vertical lines would still lead to numerical problems.

The *implicit* line equation will deal with lines of any slope. It is

$$ax + by + c = 0$$

and it is usually *normalized*, that is, a, b and c are multiplied through by $1/\sqrt{(a^2 + b^2)}$. After normalization the new values of the coefficients a and b have the property that $a^2 + b^2 = 1$, and the constant c corresponds to the perpendicular distance from the line to the origin. The implicit equation is particularly useful if we wish to decide whether a point lies on one side of the line or the other. If we are given a point (x_J, y_J), then the expression $ax_J + by_J + c$ is negative if the point is one side of the line, zero if it is on the line, and positive if it is on the other side (Figure 2.5). Two points for

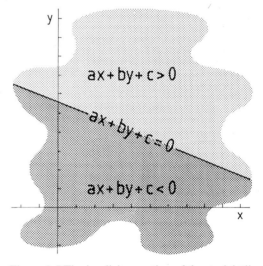

Figure 2.5 The implicit equation of the straight line divides the plane into two regions. (The inequalities assume that a and b are positive.)

which $ax_J + by_J + c$ has the same sign are on the same side of the line. (If the line equation is normalized, the absolute value of $ax_J + by_J + c$ corresponds to the point's true distance from the line.) This is an efficient and numerically stable way of cutting the plane up into two regions, one on either side of the line, and the extension of this idea into three dimensions is an important part of Chapter 7.

In the types of two-dimensional systems that we are going to discuss in this chapter, a more

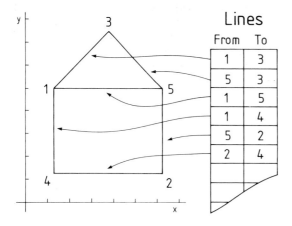

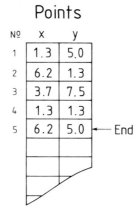

Figure 2.6 A line drawing stored as line segment records, each of which refers to two point records which contain coordinate data

frequent requirement is to represent pieces, or *segments*, of straight lines. The easiest way to do this is to specify the coordinates of a segment's endpoints. Alternatively, if we already have the point coordinates stored, a straight line segment can be defined simply by specifying two point records. Figure 2.6 shows a simple line drawing and a corresponding data structure based on this idea: it looks more like something that an engineer might recognize than the field full of flowers.

There is a less obvious way of representing line segments that can be very useful. It uses the *parametric* equation of the straight line (Figure 2.7):

$$x = x_0 + ft$$
$$y = y_0 + gt$$

We have introduced a new variable, or *parameter*, t, in addition to x and y (x_0, y_0, f and g are constants). For every value of t we can use the equations to calculate values of x and y which are points on the line. The parameter t thus changes value *along* the line. If we set t equal to 0 then we generate the point (x_0, y_0). That is why the constants x_0 and y_0 are written in the way they are. The coefficients f and g determine the slope of the line: g/f is equal to the value of m in the explicit equation. They also determine the rate at which the parameter t changes along the line. It is possible to normalize the parametric equation by multiplying both f and g (but not x_0 or y_0) by $1/\sqrt{(f^2 + g^2)}$, and then the magnitude of a change in t corresponds to a real distance moved along the line.

In Chapter 4 the idea of a parametric equation will be considerably extended as the basis of a range of smooth curves. As a straight line equation, however, the parametric form allows us to define a segment simply as the two values of t which correspond to the segment's start and end points. This is not a particularly efficient way to define a single segment, but if we wish to define a whole series of segments of the same line, on the other hand, each extra segment may be specified in half the space that would be needed to store its endpoint

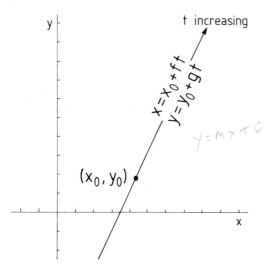

Figure 2.7 The parametric equation of the straight line. (The direction of increasing *t* assumes that *f* and *g* are positive.)

coordinates, and the segments' collinearity is automatically established.

Circles and arcs

The circle is well known by its implicit equation

$$(x - x_C)^2 + (y - y_C)^2 - r^2 = 0$$

which describes a circle centred at (x_C, y_C) and with radius r. Like the implicit straight line, this equation is ideally suited to determining whether a point is inside or outside the circle (Figure 2.8). On the other hand, the parametric circle equations

$$x = x_C + r \cos \theta$$
$$y = y_C + r \sin \theta$$

allow points on the circumference of the circle to be generated from appropriate values of the angle parameter θ. One or more arcs can be defined, in a way similar to the definition of line segments, by specifying successive values of θ. Because the circle is a closed curve the definition of segments is incomplete without a further piece of information: a convention as to whether arcs are defined clockwise or (more usually) anticlockwise.

A problem with the parametric form is that values of $\sin \theta$ and $\cos \theta$ must be calculated in a computer by summing terms in a series, and this is rather slow. An alternative circle parameterization which avoids this is

$$x = x_C + r \,\frac{1 - t^2}{1 + t^2}$$

$$y = y_C + r \,\frac{2t}{1 + t^2}$$

where $t = \tan (\theta/2)$.

The two parameterizations are compared diagrammatically in Figure 2.9. Arc segments can be defined, drawn and manipulated using t and never requiring a tangent to be calculated.

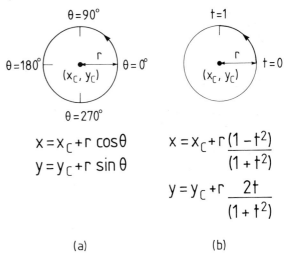

(a)   (b)

Figure 2.9 Parameterization of the circle in terms of (a) angle and (b) tangent half-angle (t). Values of t are normally restricted to $0 \leqslant t \leqslant 1$, where the parameterization is well-behaved. Larger arcs can be indicated by a convention, of which details are given in ref. 11

However, intervals in t do not of course correspond to equal angular intervals around the circle. Therefore an arc will look uneven if it is drawn by connecting points generated from large equal increments of t.

Relations between points, lines and circles

The last three sections have given brief indications of the way in which elementary pieces of Cartesian geometry may be put into

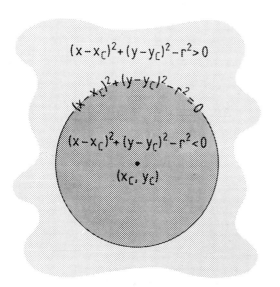

Figure 2.8 The implicit equation of the circle. Like that of the line, it divides the plane into two regions

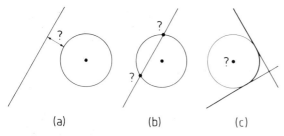

Figure 2.10 Diagrammatic examples of the three common types of geometric operation: (a) finding a distance, (b) finding intersections, and (c) creating new structures from existing geometry

the computer. It is also necessary to have reliable algorithms to act on these simple geometric elements. Even limiting these to the point, line and circle, there is a huge range of useful computations. They are dealt with in detail in ref. 11, but may be summarized as shown in Figure 2.10:

(a) Finding the distance between two geometric elements. Finding distances from a point to lines, circles and their segments is particularly important, because these calculations must be done so that we can point at parts of a picture, as our botanist pointed to his flowers. We have already seen some of the complications that arise when doing this calculation on points alone.

(b) Finding intersections. In general this leads to algebraic problems. These may be somewhat simplified if parametric as well as implicit equations are available, when the parametric expressions for x and y can be substituted into the implicit equation. For instance, to find the intersection between a line and a circle we may take the parametric line

$$x = x_0 + ft$$
$$y = y_0 + gt$$

and the implicit circle

$$(x - x_C)^2 + (y - y_C)^2 - r^2 = 0$$

Substituting the parametric line equations for x and y in the implicit circle equation, we obtain

$$(x_0 + ft - x_C)^2 + (y_0 + gt - y_C)^2 - r^2 = 0$$

which is a quadratic in t, and thus not difficult to solve.

(c) Creating new structures. A common example is the positioning of a fillet radius at a corner formed by two straight lines. There are many possibilities in this category, and a lot of algebra is involved in the solution of some of them.

Graphics devices

This is not supposed to be a book about computer graphics, but it is necessary at this point to say a few words about the various types of computer graphics device that are available, in order to explain the substantial influence that their characteristics have had on the design of programs to use shape information. The influence of device type is most profound on two-dimensional systems. Their mode of operation emphasizes fast interaction with the user in the manipulation of relatively simple structures, rather than longer computations on the more complete shape models that we shall discuss later in the book.

In addition to the *interactive* devices mentioned below, *plotters* are also needed to produce permanent copies. They may employ ink pens moved over the paper by electric motors, or somewhat more sophisticated technology borrowed from photocopiers, printers or photography. These devices have many differences, including their abilities to handle colour, size of paper and plotting speed. They are discussed at length in Newman and Sproull[47] and Foley and Van Dam,[27] but not here, where we focus on the way in which graphics devices allow us to interact directly with shape representations.

Displays

There are three types of *display* in common use, and these are compared diagrammatically in Figure 2.11. The earliest interactive computer graphics device to emerge was the *vector refresh* display. This is a development of the cathode-ray oscilloscope commonly used for testing electronic equipment. Instead of using the cathode-ray tube to examine a changing voltage, known voltages are applied to the tube's electrodes so as to draw a picture on the screen. The picture is stored as a list of line

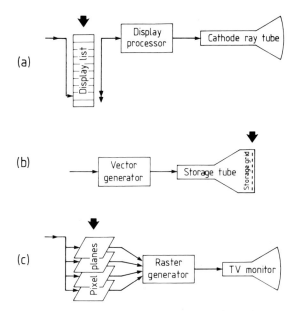

Figure 2.11 A diagrammatic comparison between graphics displays: (a) vector refresh, (b) storage tube, and (c) raster scan devices. The arrow in each diagram indicates the location of the 'permanent' picture data in that type of display

segments, and possibly characters, in digital memory. This memory may be shared with a host computer but is more frequently housed in the display itself. The memory is read again and again very quickly: in fact sufficiently fast to redraw the picture before it fades from the phosphor coating on the inside of the screen. This *refresh rate* is commonly fifty times a second. Each picture component on the *display list* is converted by fast digital-to-analogue converters into appropriately changing voltages at the deflection plates in the cathode-ray tube. Of course there is a limit to the length of display list which can be accommodated without the image appearing to flicker, but modern devices are capable of handling tens of thousands of line segments. Because the picture is updated many times a second it is easy to delete parts of it, simply by removing them from the list. Parts of a picture can almost as easily be moved around the screen, achieving some impressive animation effects. It is also possible to vary the electron beam intensity to produce lines of different brightness. The *penetron* display has two layers of

phosphor on the inside of the screen which enables variations in beam voltage to produce a small range of different colours, usually something like red, amber, yellow and green.

The *storage tube* display was originally conceived as a cheap alternative to vector refresh, which was initially a very expensive technology because of its requirement for memory and fast electronics. The storage tube display has greatly simplified electronics because it stores the picture actually inside a specially made cathode-ray tube. A storage tube has two electron guns and a fine metal mesh, called the storage grid, just behind the screen. One electron gun, called the writing cathode, draws the picture by generating a fine beam which is moved over the storage grid and discharges it locally. The electrons from a second gun, the flood cathode, are able to pass through these gaps and make a visible copy of the discharged regions of the grid on the screen phosphor. This special design of tube means that much slower beam deflection electronics can be used, and that there is potentially no limit on the complexity of a picture. Unfortunately, the design also prohibits the erasure of individual pieces of a picture: the entire screen must be cleared at one go by recharging the control grid. In general there is also no possibility of variation in colour or intensity. The system shown in Figure 2.13 is based around a storage tube display.

The most recently popular, and now most common, type of graphics device is the *raster-scan* display. This works on the same principle as a television, producing a picture by causing an electron beam to traverse the screen of a cathode-ray tube in closely spaced parallel lines—the so-called raster. In a graphics display, each line is divided into tiny pieces, or dots, which are called *pixels* (or pels), short for 'picture elements'. The picture is redrawn typically twenty-five times a second, just like a television, and one or more bits of digital memory are read to determine the state of each pixel each time it is drawn. If there is only one bit of memory per pixel, then that dot is either black or white. We usually consider a single bit per pixel to constitute a *pixel plane* of memory.

Raster-scan displays may have a number of pixel planes, which can be used to store more than one picture. Alternatively, the bits corresponding to each pixel may be considered together as a single binary number, which allows each pixel to exhibit a range of different intensities or colours. Originally, multi-plane raster-scan displays were fabulously expensive because of the huge amount of memory required to store a high-resolution picture with many colours. As computer memory has become very much cheaper this cost has become minimal relative to the cost of the other electronics and the tube, and raster-scan displays have the enormous advantage of using television tube technology for which a vast market and mass-produced components already exist. Cheap microcomputers manufactured for the domestic market now commonly include a simple integral raster-scan display sharing memory with the host microprocessor and producing the picture on an ordinary television. Systems of this quality produce a very 'grainy' picture with a few crude colours. More sophisticated displays can produce pictures made up of millions of pixels, and with a range of colours that is only limited by the phosphors on the cathode ray tube. (Of course, devices of this resolution can no longer use broadcast standard monitors.) Whatever the resolution and number of colours available, raster-scan devices have the unique ability to display pictures with areas of colour as well as lines, and it is possible to start to approach the realism of a photograph. Erasing parts of a picture is easy too: it is simply necessary to change the colours of the appropriate pixels. However, the sheer number of these, especially in high resolution displays, can put something of a brake on interactive use. The workstation shown in Figure 2.14 uses a raster-scan display (as well as a raster-scan visual display unit, for text only).

The three types of graphics display have some quite distinct properties when used interactively to edit shape information. Storage tubes, with their high resolution, were for some time the most common type of display. The necessity for frequent redrawing of the entire picture that the storage tube imposes is a considerable handicap when we are dealing with shapes, and hence pictures, that are at all complicated. More recent storage tube displays keep a copy of the drawing data in a local memory to offset this disadvantage. Vector

refresh devices avoid this difficulty, of course, but the limit on the number of line segments that can be displayed may lead to problems, for instance if a lot of hatching is required. Raster-scan displays have problems too, one of which is lower resolution, although this is being overcome on newer displays. They have also been unpopular with engineers because of their perceived poor line quality. Lines which are not horizontal, vertical or at 45 degrees appear to be jagged, or 'staircased'. (The micro-computer output in Figure 7.6 shows particularly blatant staircasing.) Staircasing can be counteracted by higher resolution, or by so-called *anti-aliasing*. This involves using colours which are a mixture of the colour of a line and the background. Pixels are coloured with denser shades if they lie right on the middle of the line, and less dense if they are further away. The eye is fooled into seeing a smooth line or curve. Of course, a prerequisite for anti-aliasing is a display that has many pixel planes.

Input devices

As well as the display itself, the design of an interactive system is affected by the input devices with which the user will be supplied. A keyboard is usual, although some system designers go out of their way to avoid the need for this as far as possible. Some method of pointing at things in the picture is essential, and this usually involves a *graphics cursor*. A cursor consists of a pair of cross-wires, like a gunsight, or some other symbol that can be moved around the screen. It can be controlled in a number of ways. Two thumbwheels (just visible to the right of the keyboard in Figure 2.13), one for the x and one for the y direction, are common. Alternatives include a *joystick*, like a model aircraft controller (an example appears in the bottom right-hand corner of Figure 2.14), a tablet, or a mouse. A *tablet* detects the position of a pen (or sometimes a puck, a little ring set with a window and cross-hairs) on a specially constructed surface, while a *mouse* is a little box that can be pushed across a desk, and has wheels in its base which signal the movements made. A *light pen* is a rather different device, which is not tied to the use of a cursor. It is simply a photocell on a stick which can be pointed at a vector on a refresh display, or a pixel on a raster-scan display. It uses the display timing to discover at which vector or pixel the user is pointing.

There are essentially two modes in which these interactive devices can be used: picking and locating. *Picking* is the selection of some part of the picture already on the screen. A light pen used with a vector refresh display is able to identify an item on the display list directly. When a cursor is in use, on the other hand, the computer must search through the entire picture data to find what part of it is nearest to the cursor coordinates. We have already seen that programming such searches efficiently is not trivial.

However it is implemented, the action of picking is useful to select part of the picture so as to indicate the scope of some change that is to be made. That could be as simple as a change of colour, or an instruction to delete half the picture. Alternatively, picking can be used in conjunction with specially drawn symbols, which are not part of the picture proper, as a way of controlling the program being run: an alternative to a command language. The most common example of this is the *menu*, which is simply a list of commands. The person using the program points to the menu item corresponding to the action he wants the program to take next. On vector refresh and raster-scan displays the menu can be changed quickly to correspond with different phases of a program. Storage tubes present a problem in this respect: no one will take kindly to waiting for a large engineering drawing to be redrawn every time the menu changes. It is possible, but messy, actually to cross out parts of the menu that are no longer valid, and to add new options on to the end. A more common solution is to provide a graphics tablet with a pre-printed menu card permanently attached. The workstation in Figure 2.13 has this arrangement. This effectively increases the area available for user interaction, because a stylus position on the tablet can be interpreted as pointing to the picture or to the menu, as appropriate.

While picking chooses from among existing parts of a picture, *locating* is the specification of a new coordinate position, at which something can be drawn. This is the way in which graphics cursors naturally operate. On the other hand, a light pen attached to a vector refresh display is useless when pointed at a blank screen. For a light pen to act as a locating device it is necessary to introduce a dummy symbol on the screen, usually a cross. The arms of this *tracking cross* are made up of different elements from the display list, and so the computer can detect which arm the light pen is pointing at. The computer moves the tracking cross so as to centralize it, and thus the cross follows the light pen across the screen— providing it is not moved too fast. The computer knows the position of the cross, and so the combination of light pen and tracking cross enables the user to specify coordinate positions almost as easily as with a cursor.

The action of locating is commonly associated with the creation of new parts of a picture. When a position has been specified it can be used as the end of a line segment perhaps, or as the centre of a circle. It is possible for the line segments that are being defined by a new coordinate to be redrawn quickly, on an appropriate type of display, while the cursor or tracking cross is actually being moved around the screen. The lines then appear to stretch like 'rubber bands', and this technique allows a very fast visual assessment of a construction. In CAE, it is more usual that precise coordinate values are required, but graphical locating techniques can still be useful with a grid, as explained later in this chapter.

Draughting systems

The most widespread, and in a sense the most obvious, engineering application for graphics devices is in the automation of the functions of a drawing board and other drawing instruments. There are many advantages claimed for these *draughting systems*, especially the speed at which a drawing can be prepared. Actually they often have little advantage over conventional techniques in the preparation of a completely new drawing, but most draughting involves a great number of bits of drawing which are either identical to, or systematic variations on, one another. Using a draughting system, most repetitive work can be automated, and this is where the big savings in time

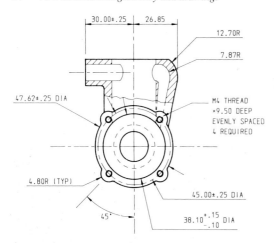

Figure 2.12 Part of a detail drawing of a diecasting for a model aircraft engine, produced on a draughting system. (Radan Computational Ltd)

(and boredom) occur. The other dramatic improvement over drawing on paper is the ability to erase mistakes or otherwise to alter drawings and then to obtain a perfect copy. Even a drastic redesign may not require much editing, when making a fresh start would be the only sensible thing using conventional techniques. The quality of output from draughting systems is illustrated by the detail drawing in Figure 2.12.

A number of basic features are common to draughting systems of all types. Many draughting systems are designed for a particular market, however, and therefore contain extra features peculiar to a single technical activity. In the following sections we shall discuss only the most general type of draughting system, which might be advertised as suitable for mechanical engineering, architectural and civil engineering applications, and also for the production of diagrams for technical illustration. Of the other more specialist systems, those for printed circuit board and integrated circuit layout and those for cartography are of considerable importance. Both of these types of system must be capable of handling much more data than a general system, and so data structuring considerations are of prime importance. Draughting systems for integrated circuit design are currently seen as essential to that technology, and not just a cost-effective

alternative to manual techniques. The geometry is simple, but the quantity of data is often enormous: drawings may take days to plot. The availability of colour on the screen is essential to help the user make sense of so many similar shapes, and to differentiate between the layers on a printed circuit board or integrated circuit. Draughting systems for electronics keep a record of circuit connectivity, as well as geometric information, and circuit analysis routines are included in most systems.

Because draughting systems are a computerization of a manual process there is a requirement for more dialogue, that is commands and responses, between the user and his system than is the case with systems which can do more for themselves. The graphics devices which a system uses are therefore of primary importance, and so are the programming techniques by which interaction is managed. The pure calculation, or 'number-crunching', load imposed on the computer on which a draughting system is running, on the other hand, is generally lower than that generated by the use of more sophisticated shape representations. For this reason, and because draughtsmen are full-time users of their system, it is most satisfactory to provide a separate microprocessor to drive each draughtsman's graphics display. Together with interactive input devices, this equipment is often called a *workstation*. Figure 2.13 shows a 'stand-alone' configuration. The workstation of Figure 2.14, on the other hand, also has a local microprocessor, but is designed for connection to a central computer to share access to data and more complex programs than the local microprocessor can run.

Fundamental structures

All draughting systems with any claim to generality must have points, line segments, circles and arcs available as a minimum range of geometric elements. We have already seen, at the beginning of this chapter, how these can be stored in a computer. The precise choice of representations is part of the skill of a system designer, bearing in mind the equipment on

Figure 2.13 A configuration of equipment for running a draughting system. The storage tube type display shares its cabinet with a microcomputer, 'floppy' discs are used to store programs and drawing data, and a plotter is provided so that paper copies can be made. (Radan Computational Ltd)

Figure 2.14 Equipment comprising a 'workstation' for connection to a central computer. The raster scan display (centre) is for the drawing, while the second screen (right) is for text, thus keeping the drawing area clear. In the foreground (from left to right) are a keyboard, a tablet with a pre-printed menu on it and a joystick. (Cambridge Interactive Systems Ltd)

which his software will run. Generalization is made more difficult by the (understandable) commercial secrecy surrounding draughting systems, and there will be no attempt here to itemize the components of a typical system. Whatever the data structure chosen, additional information normally has to be associated with the geometric data. Different line types are common and are particularly important in preparing drawings. The line types available may include different widths, colours, and various types of broken line. Often different line attributes are appropriate for a graphics display and for plotting a drawing on paper.

In addition to straight lines and curves, draughting systems must allow a drawing to be annotated with text. It would be both inefficient and confusing to treat each line segment of each character as an individual part of the drawing just like, say, the outline of the component. Instead, we want the ability to refer to a character or a whole line of text as a single entity, and in this way we can also save space storing the text and time accessing it. Arrangements must then be made for text to have its own part of the data structure, distinct from geometry. It is also necessary to associate each piece of text with another, simpler, piece of geometry that we can use as a 'handle', so that we can refer to it in a graphical way. We could for instance specify a single point, say the bottom left-hand corner of a line of text, as its handle. Such a simple scheme has, as ever, a number of problems. It may be that the first few words of text are off the left-hand edge of the screen. Although the rest of the line is visible, the cursor cannot get at the point and so we are stuck with the visible portion of the line of text as it is. Again, with a single point as handle, we can only position the text and not orientate it, at least not graphically. A better solution might be, for instance, to use a rectangular box around the whole line as the handle.

Layers

An engineering drawing is a rather cluttered combination of pieces of geometry and text all fulfilling different functions. Part of the skill of reading a drawing is to be able to identify and to separate the functions of the various types of construction. In a draughting system the parts of the drawing with different functions may be identified within the data structure as a number of levels, or *layers*. Imagine that different types of line, say outlines, extension lines and dimension lines, as well as the different types of text, are all drawn on a number of layers of transparent film. A layer on the computer may be turned off and on just like removing and replacing one of these pieces of film. This is a considerable bonus to the draughtsman in organizing his drawing. Firms that use draughting systems often have company standards for the use of layers, and this makes drawings stored in the computer easier for a draughtsman's colleagues to read or modify. Figure 2.15 shows the four layers that were used in the construction of Figure 2.12. The logic of the separation is readily apparent. Additionally, a single component outline may be used for more than one purpose by attaching two or more different sets of dimensions and annotations, each on its own layer: one for machining and one for inspection, for example.

Layers are also very useful in system operation. A function which uses the cursor can be associated with a number of layers, on which the part of the picture to be found is known to lie. The search can then be greatly restricted by looking through the data items on those layers alone. If, for instance, the user indicates that he wishes to delete a dimension line, the system only has to search the layer assigned to dimension lines to find the line nearest to the cursor position. A pointless search of, say, segments of the outline, is avoided altogether.

Fundamental facilities

The really fundamental facilities of a draughting system are those by which the geometry is created. Having decided which line and curve types are available, it is necessary to provide functions to allow them to be inserted, on the appropriate layer, and deleted when necessary. It is not difficult to see how a point or a straight line could be created using coordinates from the graphics cursor. Arcs are more difficult to control. There are a number of methods to input an arc by specifying three or more points, and they all involve making some of the data

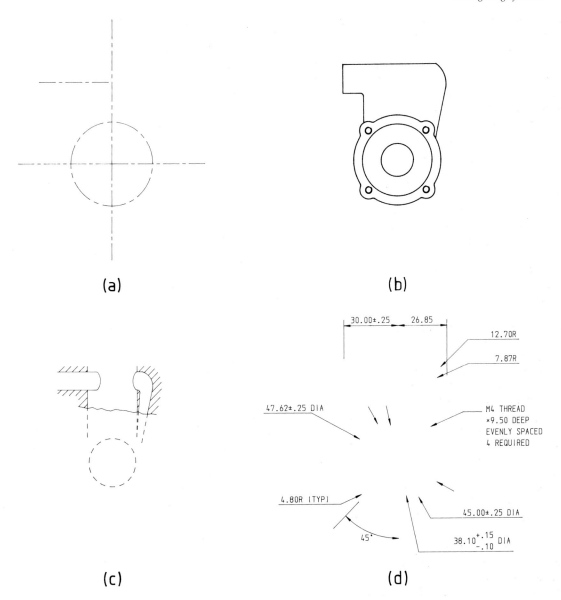

(a)

(b)

(c)

(d)

Figure 2.15 A separation of the four layers on which the drawing of Figure 2.12 was constructed. The layers contain (a) centre lines, (b) the outline, (c) section details, including hatching lines, and (d) dimensioning. (Radan Computational Ltd)

from the cursor redundant. (The control of more general curves from points is a major topic of Chapter 4.) Similar facilities must also be available to position text and symbols. Text also requires justification and centring.

In most cases, features must be specified accurately, and cursor coordinates are inadequate. Coordinate values may of course be typed in, but this is very time-consuming. One very useful alternative is to specify a *grid*, a regular pattern of lines, and then to have the system constrain all points input from the cursor to be positioned at the nearest intersection of grid lines. Useful grid patterns (Figure 2.16) are regularly spaced vertical and horizontal straight lines, or a polar grid consisting of a

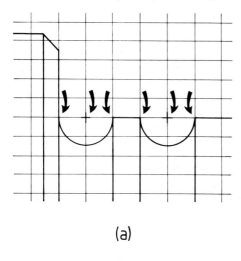

(a)

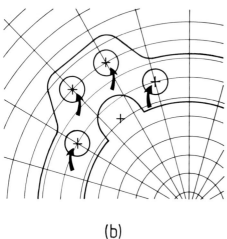

(b)

Figure 2.16 (a) Cartesian and (b) polar grid patterns. The arrows indicate points located on the grids

pattern of circles and radial lines. The grid lines need not be displayed, of course, even when the grid is in use. Usually, a single grid is only useful for a small part of a drawing, and it must be possible easily to define new grids as required.

Point coordinates may also be obtained from geometry already on the drawing. At the simplest, this means re-using the end of an existing line segment. More taxing is to determine the coordinates of the intersection of two lines or curves, where the appropriate geometric calculation must be performed by the system. More powerful facilities are provided when new lines or curves can be created directly from the geometry already present. *Filleting* is the most common example of this. A fillet is an arc which is positioned so as to round off the corner formed by two lines or curves. Like the calculation of intersections, such facilities require quite a lot of computer code to implement, because of the number of possible different lines and curves between any pair of which a fillet may be required. There are further potential problems with filleting over and above the basic geometric construction. These include the case shown in Figure 2.17 where the fillet selected is too large for one of the segments between which it should be placed. Draughting systems should allow for such possibilities and take sensible action when error conditions occur.

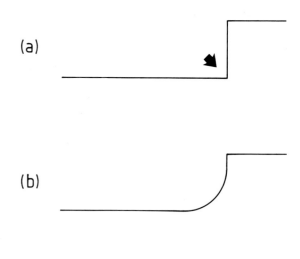

(a)

(b)

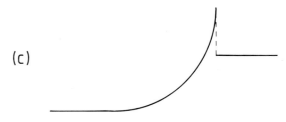

(c)

Figure 2.17 A problem with automatic filleting. The user indicates (a) that a corner (arrowed) is to be filleted. This is perfectly feasible with (b) a reasonable radius, but (c) what action should the system take if the radius specified is too large?

Similar time-saving facilities are often available for constructions relating to the particular applications for which a draughting system was designed. In mechanical engineering systems the most common such facility is the partially automatic layout of dimensions and tolerances. Instead of having to draw every set of extension and dimension lines separately, and then positioning the numerical values just like any other text, many draughting systems contain routines to perform these repetitive tasks with the minimum input from the user. They can ensure that dimensioning corresponds to the appropriate drawing standards, and may also perform conversions between different units.

When working with large drawings a great deal of the detail is lost if all of the drawing is on the screen at once. In particular, text needs to be quite large (five pixels high is an absolute minimum on a raster display) to be readable at all. In order to get around this problem, it is essential to be able to use the graphics screen as a *window* to display just a part of the whole drawing: in other words, to be able to *zoom* down to areas of interest. Problems met in zooming include determining sensible ways to display symbols and text in close up. Facilities for zooming are often not infinitely variable, in order to avoid precisely such difficulties. Most draughting systems incorporate knowledge of standard sheet sizes, and many require a user to select one when he starts a drawing. This restriction is sweetened by facilities for incorporating company standard sheet layout, logos and so on.

Profiles and hatching

The *profile* is a common higher level structure formed from a list of line segments and arcs arranged in a closed curve (Figure 2.18). These lists can be created by the user by pointing, in the appropriate order, to the segments which are to comprise the profile. (Many systems have the ability to check that a profile really does correspond to a closed curve.) The most common use for the profile in engineering draughting systems is to facilitate automatic cross-hatching. Even though a profile has to be defined, a hatching function is obviously a considerable saving in time over the creation of each hatching line individually. Hatching routines are not complex. In essence (Figure 2.19) they use maximum and minimum coordinate information to determine the extent of

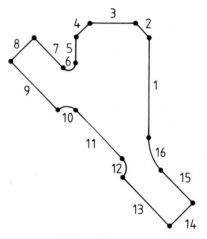

Figure 2.18 A profile constructed from 12 straight-line segments and four arcs taken in the order indicated

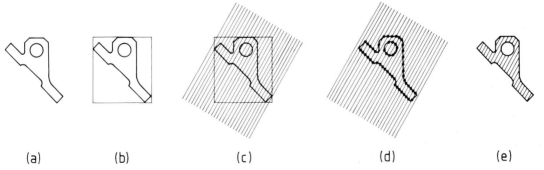

(a) (b) (c) (d) (e)

Figure 2.19 Automatic cross-hatching of two nested profiles (a). A box (b) is constructed around the profiles, a pattern of lines (c) is generated, intersections (d) are found and sorted, and (e) the hatching lines are truncated at these intersection points

the profile. This information is then used to generate a sufficient number of straight lines to cover the profile, at the appropriate angle and pitch. Each of these lines is compared with each edge of the profile, and the intersections found and ordered. Odd-numbered intersections correspond to the start of hatching line segments, even-numbered intersections terminate them. This procedure will cope with both nested and self-intersecting profiles.

Symbols and copying

We have already said that one of the most important parts of a draughting system is the ability to copy repeated parts of a drawing, rather than to have to draw them again. If a drawing contains a major portion that is symmetrical about a centre line, for instance, then making a mirror image can halve the work involved. The part of the drawing that is to be mirrored may be determined by placing it alone on a layer, or by some other method such as drawing a rectangle around the elements to be replicated. This facility can be extended by allowing elements which originate outside the current drawing to be copied onto it, either from another drawing or from a library of symbols. *Symbols* are simply frequently used pieces of drawing, such as the plan view of the head of a nut, or an elevation of a standard window frame. Symbol libraries may be created by a draughtsman for his own convenience or be held centrally for a whole company. The latter approach has obvious benefits in terms of standardization and control of variety.

Various *transformations* (Figure 2.20) are required when positioning symbols (and also when copying within a drawing, of course). It must be possible to *shift* the symbol to the required place on the screen, and to *rotate* it through an angle. Reversed copies of the symbol may be created by *mirroring*, which saves creating and storing left- and right-handed versions separately. Most symbols will also be required in more than one size. *Uniform scaling* just makes a symbol larger or smaller, while *unidirectional scaling* can be used to stretch or squash it. This is useful to make the symbol fit in a particular place, but sometimes has unfortunate results. For instance, if a symbol represents a side view of a bolt, then scaling the length by a factor of two does not produce a longer bolt of the same series: the head will be too deep. Unidirectional scaling of arcs is a problem, too: ellipses are seldom the result required. For these sorts of object many systems provide a language in which the geometry of families of components can be described. When a component from the family is required, a small program, written in what is called a *macro language*, is run which determines all its dimensions from a number of key sizes. For a bolt, the key sizes might be the

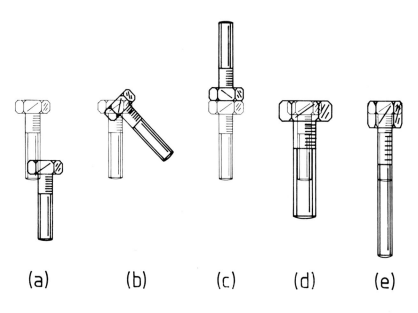

(a)   (b)   (c)   (d)   (e)

Figure 2.20 A symbol representing a side view of a bolt transformed by (a) shifting, (b) rotation, (c) mirroring, (d) scaling, and (e) unidirectional scaling. The narrow lines show the symbol before and the thick lines the symbol after transformation

thread pitch and its length. Such *parameterized* symbols are relatively difficult to create as some programming is needed, but well worth the effort for features common to many drawings. Draughting systems for producing electrical and electronic schematic drawings would be almost useless without a huge number of parameterized symbols for common components.

A major consideration when using symbols is how the symbol data is incorporated onto the drawing. Every piece of geometry in the symbol can be separately copied into the data structure of the drawing. Alternatively a reference to the symbol, and the position in which it was placed, may be recorded. The first procedure is essential if a symbol is subsequently to be modified, but it prohibits the symbol from being moved or deleted as a whole once it is in position. Creating a reference to a single copy of a symbol, stored elsewhere, is more flexible but incurs an overhead in retrieving the symbol definition every time it is required. With the latter approach, a symbol that is, say, a company standard may be changed once centrally, and this effectively changes every drawing that contains it. Many systems allow symbols to be themselves constructed from other symbols, and so on. In this case, efficiency requires that the way in which symbols are stored be carefully considered.

3

From two to three dimensions

Readers with engineering backgrounds may be wondering what can be in the rest of this book. The communication of the shape of a product between engineers has become synonymous with the traditional engineering drawing, like music and the five-line stave. In the last chapter we examined ways in which the computer can indeed be used to assist the draughtsman, so surely that is the end of the matter? That might be true if we only wanted to use computers to accelerate the rate at which engineers can communicate between themselves and with craftsmen. But computers are also capable of being programmed to assist more directly in designing and making a component, by determining its properties for instance, or by controlling a machine to make it. To perform these tasks a shape representation is necessary from which programs can easily extract the shape information that they need. The problem with the engineering drawing in this respect is that it assumes that its readers have an almost cultural familiarity with drawing conventions and also with the sorts of shape features which engineering components usually have. It has so far proved impossible to make a program behave in anything like such an intelligent way. The most promising attempts so far have succeeded only in identifying a very simple shape from a number of accurate and unannotated views,[55,72] which is not the same thing at all. Even if it were possible to write a program that could read drawings, it would hardly be sensible to attach

such a complex process to the front of every program that needed shape information. We would still require a more computable internal shape representation to which drawings could be converted and from which other programs could extract information without too much difficulty. We call such computer-orientated shape representations *shape models*. Simple shape models, like the ones we are going to examine in this chapter, are not difficult for people to understand or to create, and programs using them run quite fast. Some of the techniques in later chapters, on the other hand, lead to quite complex programs which

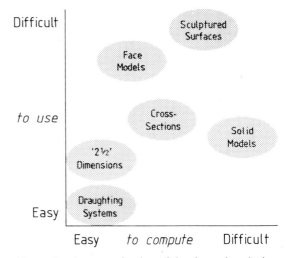

Figure 3.1 A categorization of the shape description techniques mentioned in this book

use a lot of computer time, but these models can represent more complex shapes more completely. What all computer-based shape models have in common is at least some suitability for use by both man and machine. Figure 3.1 places some of the representations that appear in this book within a somewhat subjective plot of acceptability to the user against 'computability'—a combined measure of how easily programs can be written and how quickly they run. Note that important considerations like the types of shape that can be modelled are conveniently omitted.

Two-dimensional models

While a drawing is two-dimensional, solid things never are. That is why we always need more than one view in a engineering drawing. However, some engineering components can be defined *almost* completely by two-dimensional geometry. A piece cut out of sheet material may be enormously complex but in an engineering drawing that complexity can be drawn in a single view: the second view only needs to show the material thickness. The sheet need not be metal: the same applies to plastics, plywood, and flexible materials like leather and fabric. Slightly less obviously, a component turned on a lathe can also be defined in two dimensions by its outline, although the usual engineering drawing convention for this class of shapes rather confuses the issue. A lot of components are cut from sheet or turned, and so two-dimensional shape models are very useful, although we must remember that as soon as we bend a piece of sheet metal, or drill a cross-bore in a turned component, we need a different approach.

The simplest two-dimensional model is probably a list of holes to be drilled in a piece of sheet. This model is merely a list of occurrences, or *instances* of a single type of shape, albeit in different sizes. Designing a corresponding data-structure is hardly taxing, provided that we can overcome the problems with lists that have already been mentioned in Chapter 2. Nor are such systems useless: programs are used in the design and manufacture of heat-exchanger endplates, where thousands of holes are required in specific

patterns. Printed circuit boards are another example. We assume, or the computer can check, that all the holes are disjoint. As soon as two holes intersect each other a new shape is created, which cannot be modelled in the same way.

The next simplest components to model are probably those that can be represented by a single boundary which does not intersect itself. A boundary can represent a solid extrusion, a piece of sheet material (without holes) or a turned component (Figure 3.2). The model of

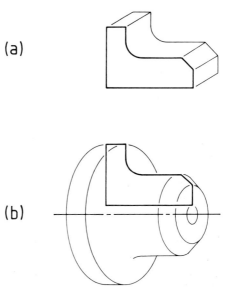

Figure 3.2 A boundary interpreted as (a) an 'extrusion', or (b) a 'turned component'

an extrusion or sheet component is completed by specifying the length or thickness of the material. To interpret a boundary as a turned component the axis of revolution must be specified. The most common way of modelling shapes of this sort is to use the profile structure which has already been described, as a draughting system facility, in Chapter 2. In draughting systems the profile is used to define areas of a drawing, often regions to be hatched. If the shape of a length of extrusion is defined as a profile, what can the computer be programmed to do with it? The most useful simple calculation is probably to find its weight, by computing the area of the profile and multiplying that by its length and the density of the material. We can easily obtain

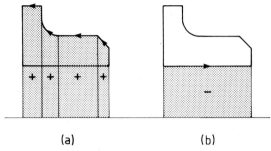

(a)   (b)

Figure 3.3 One method of calculating the area of a profile is to sum the areas between each side and a coordinate axis. The directions of the sides must be taken into account, so that sides on the 'bottom' of the profile generate areas that are subtracted from the total. Note that, with this method, numerical accuracy will suffer if the axis is a long way from the polygon

the area of a profile by combining together areas generated by each segment of its edge (Figure 3.3). The sign of an area computed in this way will change depending on whether the profile was defined clockwise or anticlockwise: calculating the area is one way of finding this out, if we don't know, but otherwise the sign can be ignored. Similar pieces of geometry will

give us surface areas, volumes, centres of gravity, principal axes and moments of inertia of both extrusions and turned components. Considering the difficulty in getting these results manually (the author has tried it), this must be as popular with designers and draughtsmen as any aspect of CAE systems!

Machining

Suppose that we are rash enough to want to manufacture the component represented by our profile. If it is to be cut from sheet we may want to flamecut, mill, punch or nibble it, or cut it with a laser or water-jet. If it is a turned part then it will most probably be produced on a lathe. Punching, extrusion and many other processes involve a master shape of some sort, but initially this must be machined. If we are using a shape model rather than a draughting system, it is likely that we are going to use a *numerically controlled* (NC) machine tool. NC machine tools have motors rather than handles attached to their axes of movement and the cutting process is controlled by means of instructions punched on tape or, on more modern machines, transmitted down a wire

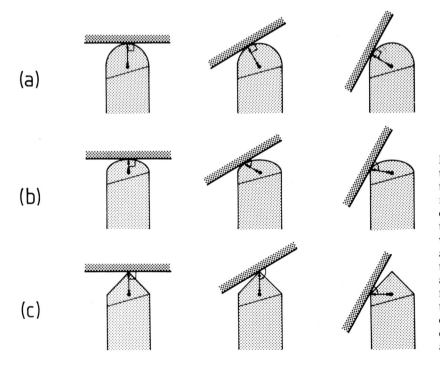

(a)

(b)

(c)

Figure 3.4 Diagrammatic pictures of lathe cutters showing that (a) a round-nosed cutter has a constant offset normal to the material surface, while (b) an elliptical and (c) a triangular cutter have offsets that vary around the cutter profile. With all lathe cutters, the shank of the cutter prevents cutting completely at some angles

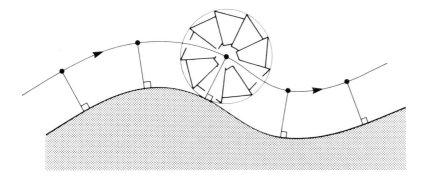

Figure 3.5 The path of the centre of a circular milling cutter is determined by offsetting a constant distance normal to the profile being cut

from a computer. As well as the cutter movements, other functions such as spindle speed and coolant flow are usually under program control, and on many machines cutters may be changed automatically. It is possible to program NC machine tools manually on a movement-by-movement basis, but our aim is to extract the required cutter movements from the shape model we have taken such trouble to create.

All cutters, including flames, laser beams and water jets, have a finite size. If we program any point on the cutter to follow a profile, then, in general, other parts of the cutter will, at some points on the profile, move inside the edge and make the final shape smaller than the one we wanted. Before cutting we therefore compute a new profile, larger than the first, which a point on the cutter can follow while its perimeter produces the profile we actually want. This process is called *offsetting* and the distance from the profile to the fixed point on the cutter is called the *offset*. Sharply pointed lathe tools, nibbling cutters and such, have different offsets at different places (Figure 3.4). Happily, we are often concerned with milling cutters, which must of course be circular. The path of the cutter centre is a constant distance from the original profile (Figure 3.5). To compute an offset from a profile it is first necessary to be able to find offsets from all the individual segments that make up its boundary. Luckily, straight line segments and circular arcs become other straight line segments and arcs of different radii under offsetting for a circular cutter. If all the segments of a profile join smoothly then the offset profile is simply the list of offset curves, but more frequently there are sharp

corners. Internal corners require part or all of the offset segments to be discarded, while external corners require that they are extended (Figure 3.6). Arcs can be introduced around external corners: this reduces the chance of the cutter path spoiling another part of the

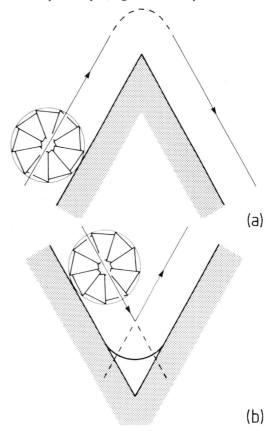

(a)

(b)

Figure 3.6 Where two segments of a profile meet, the offsets as determined from each segment individually may need to be (a) extended or (b) all or partially discarded

workpiece and minimizes the amount of 'swarf' (chips of material) produced.

The author has used a simple profile representation that makes offsetting very easy. Any closed contour consisting of arc and straight line segments can be represented as a list of circles and points (which are considered as circles of zero radius). The straight line portions of the profile are constructed as tangents between the circles, taken in the order in which they are listed. Each circle has a positive or negative sign attached to its radius to indicate whether it generates an internal or external radius. The reader might like to consider the arrangement as a series of cotton reels pinned to a board with an elastic band wound round them: clockwise round the 'positive' ones and anticlockwise around the 'negative' ones. Figure 3.7 shows a very simple component constructed using this system and the corresponding cutter path. Offsetting is

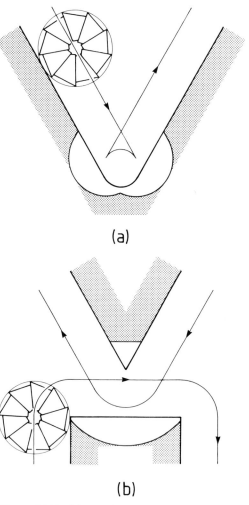

(a)

(b)

Figure 3.8 Problems with naive offsetting techniques occur (a) at sharp internal corners and (b) narrow throats, when the correct profile will not be generated

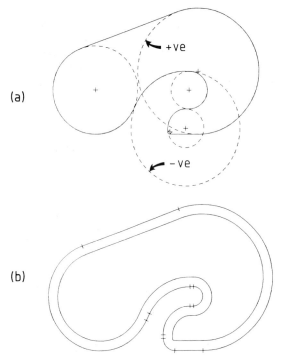

(a)

(b)

Figure 3.7 The outer profile of a crane hook represented (a) as a list of signed circles joined by tangents. One of each of the positively signed circles and of the negatively signed circles is labelled. The offset (b) is calculated by incrementing the (signed) radius of each circle and redrawing

very straightforward. Each circle has its radius increased by the cutter radius and the profile is redrawn. The signs of the circles are taken into account, and so internal radii shrink, as they should. The author has a small program[7] that uses this technique. It relies on its user to ensure that profiles are suitable for offsetting by a given radius. In a more sophisticated system, whatever profile representation is used, it is necessary to check for concavities which are of smaller radius than the cutter, internal corners and narrow throats (Figure 3.8). In all of these cases the cutter is unable to cut the entire profile, and a smaller and possibly differently shaped cutter must be used to finish it. Detecting and rectifying all these problems automatically are difficult to implement reliably. In industrial systems, automatic offsetting procedures are usually supplemented by someone looking at a plot of the cutter path. If a program were able to sort out all possible clearance problems, cutter paths would still need modification to accommodate requirements specific to the cutting process, such as leaving tabs to keep a component attached to its parent sheet while some further process is carried out, or, on a lathe, ensuring that the component is parted off from the bar in a sensible way: in particular, not before cutting has been completed!

Other applications

The need to prepare cutter paths has been the reason for developing most two-dimensional representations in mechanical engineering. In electronics, both integrated circuits and printed circuit boards provide a wealth of combinatorially very complex two-dimensional problems. There are also further mechanical engineering applications for purely two-dimensional shape models. One of the earliest uses of machine vision in industry was to recognize flat components and to identify their position and orientation. A sharp silhouette can be produced by back lighting, and a simple black and white image is then available for processing. Its area and moments of area may be calculated and compared with values obtained from a shape model. There are other statistics, such as perimeter length (very easy to get from a profile), which are of particular value for image processing. In effect, the shape information in the model is 'abstracted' for the benefit of the vision system, which is usually required to produce its results in fractions of a second. At the other extreme, profiles may be used as the basis for two-dimensional stress, or heat transfer, analysis. Here the model is expanded by dividing the profile up into a number of small pieces for boundary element analysis, or by segmenting the area inside it for finite element analysis. In both cases, many small shapes are created whose individual response to a stress or heat flow can be

predicted. Combining the behaviours of all these little models allows a (large and complex) program to predict the behaviour of the component as a whole.

Two-dimensional models are not useful solely on an individual basis. A number of shapes often have to be cut out of a large sheet. Profile models of the required components can form the data for a process known as *nesting*, which attempts to position them on the sheet so that minimum wastage occurs. This is a difficult problem which has a number of variations, depending for instance on whether discrete sheets are involved, or a roll of material, and whether the grain of the material must be aligned with the components. The number of possible arrangements is enormous and an 'optimum' solution is usually impossible. A common way to approach the problem is to fit each of the profiles to be nested within a rectangle. The rectangles are relatively easy to nest together and when this is completed the shapes are 'jiggled' into final position. An alternative is for a person to specify the coarse positions and again have the computer adjust them. This allows preferences to be met that would be difficult or time-consuming to include in the program: for instance, grouping certain profiles together. Figure 3.9 shows some very irregular profiles—parts of shoes—which have

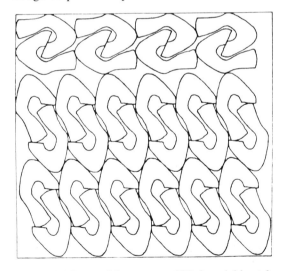

Figure 3.9 Parts of the uppers of 32 shoes laid out for cutting from a sheet of leather. This layout was produced fully automatically. (Courtesy of the Shoe and Allied Trades Research Association)

been nested together for cutting out from a sheet of leather.

'Two-and-a-half' dimensions

While turned parts are quite adequately described by a single profile, there will often be a necessity to represent holes in components made from sheet material. This requirement can be satisfied by adding further, smaller, profiles inside the first. (We have already met such an arrangement in Figure 2.19). In order for this to be a valid representation of a pierced plate, the internal profiles must not be permitted to intersect either the outer profile or each other, or to lie inside each other. We can either build checks into the system or rely on the user to verify that these conditions are met by looking at a picture. The sorts of calculations that can be performed on a single profile can be repeated for a plate with holes. It is usually convenient if the internal profiles representing holes are defined in the opposite direction to the outer profile: say clockwise and anticlockwise respectively. This means that the material is always on the same side of a segment of any of the profiles, taking its direction into account, which simplifies operations like offsetting.

If a number of profiles represent changes in the thickness of a plate, rather than holes right through it, then it is legitimate to have any number of profiles inside one another. Instead of the single thickness necessary to complete the representation of a plate we now associate a value with each profile. This value is the height of the surface of the material within that profile. The value applies until 'countermanded' by any further profiles lying inside the first. If the height associated with a profile is less than the profile surrounding it, then it represents a slot or pocket in the object. If the profile is higher then it is a plateau or island (Figure 3.10). The shapes that can be represented in this way are not truly two-dimensional, but most of the information about them is vested in the profiles which may be complicated combinations of curve types. Only the simple height values relate to the third dimension, and the imprecise but evocative term 'two-and-a-half-dimensional', or '2½D', has stuck.

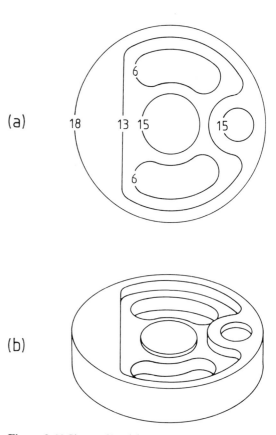

(a)

(b)

Figure 3.10 Six profiles (a) with height values attached interpreted (b) as a 'two-and-a-half-dimensional' shape

Machining

The main reason for the popularity of 2½D representations is the geometry of machining carried out on a milling machine, and the existence of a large number of NC machine tools of this type. When a cylindrical milling cutter moves either in the direction of its axis or perpendicular to it, it creates a cavity with a flat bottom and sides composed of straight line segments and arcs: in fact a 2½D shape (Figure 3.11). If we move the cutter at any other angle, then the end of the cutter creates an elliptical cylinder. Whatever its aesthetic merits, engineers generally have little use for this type of shape and therefore very often design components that can be milled in a 2½D way. Of course, more than one face of a part may be machined by using either rotary axes on the machine or multiple set-ups (turning the

that during profiling the cutter is not cutting across its entire width, which would lead to a poor surface finish on the profile walls. Where pockets are deep, both area clearance and profiling cuts must be performed in more than one pass, removing one layer of material at a time. The final, lowest, cut is often a shallow one in order to get a good finish on the horizontal surface of the component.

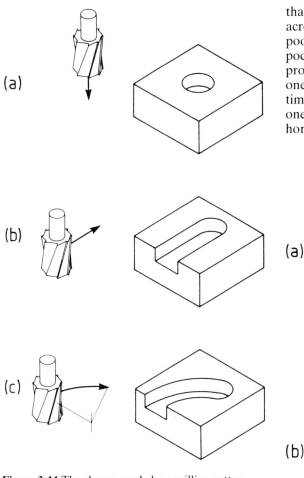

(a)

(b)

(c)

Figure 3.11 The shapes made by a milling cutter moving (a) axially, (b) in a straight line, and (c) in an arc (both the latter in the plane perpendicular to its axis)

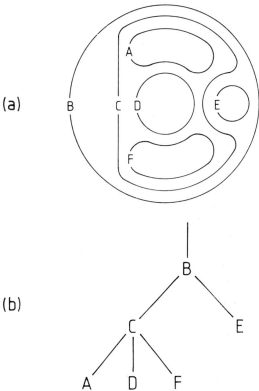

(a)

(b)

Figure 3.12 The nesting of the profiles of Figure 3.10 interpreted as a tree structure. A profile encloses the smaller profiles below it in the tree

component over and clamping it down again). In this case each such face can be considered as a separate 2½D shape.

Determining how to cut the component is the most important, indeed usually the only, application of a 2½D shape representation. It is necessary to perform two types of cutting operation. *Profiling* cuts generate the vertical faces of the profiles, using cutter paths that are derived by offsetting, as described earlier in this chapter. In addition, it is necessary to remove bulk material from inside pockets and around islands. These parts of the cutter path are called *area clearance* operations. They are usually performed before the profiling cuts so

It is possible to automate many parts of 2½D cutter path generation with some success. A set of profiles can be searched to determine which lie inside which others, and from this information it can be deduced which represent pockets and which islands. A tree structure showing how the profiles are nested may be constructed (Figure 3.12). This can tell us whether the offset for the finishing cut is to be taken inside or outside a profile, and what depth of cut is necessary. The nesting of the profiles also

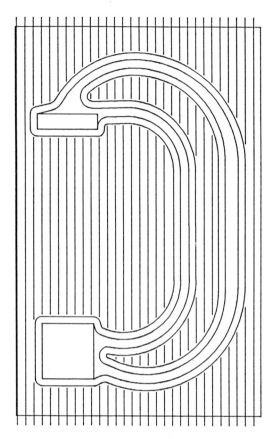

Figure 3.13 Automatically generated profiling and area clearance cutter paths at one depth used in the machining of a G-clamp pattern

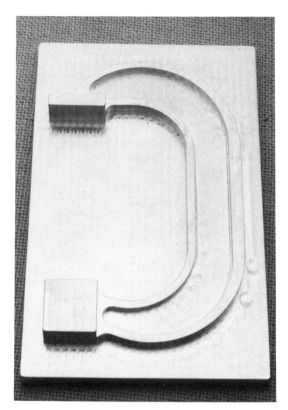

Figure 3.14 Finished G-clamp pattern machined with the cutter path of Figure 3.13, and similar paths at other levels

provides data to allow the area clearance cut to be generated. The simplest way to do this is as a series of parallel straight cutter paths, but alternatives include a spiral from the centre to the outside of a pocket.[53] Parallel cuts are essentially the same as hatching lines and can be generated in the same way (Figure 2.19). Because the centre of the tool will follow the 'hatching lines', the profile must be offset before the area clearance cutter path is generated or the cutter will gouge into the profile walls. Figure 3.13 shows part of a cutter path that was determined fully automatically from a 2½D representation, and Figure 3.14 shows the completed component, part of a pattern for a clamp.

In practice, there are many difficulties with a fully automatic system. For instance, profiles which do not touch may nevertheless be too close for a given cutter to pass between them, but a smaller cutter would take too long to complete the entire workpiece, and there can be other reasons for changing cutters during profiling. Further problems occur in area clearance. In particular, not all milling cutters can cut axially into the material (Figure 3.15). Using these cutters, the first cut at a new level must be started by a drill or by an angled descent of the cutter, called 'ramping'. Additionally, long cutters can bend when loaded unevenly, or the workpiece itself may distort at thin sections. It is difficult for an automatic system to take care of these machining considerations, and many of the most used commercial systems do not attempt to provide a high degree of automation. The GNC (Graphical Numerical Control) system[18] developed in the early seventies is typical of an interactive approach. A person using GNC starts by creating profiles with a language. The

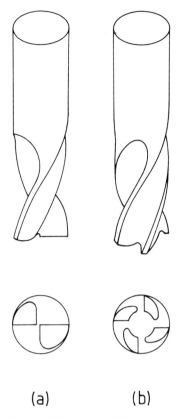

Figure 3.15 A slot drill (a) is capable of axial descents into a workpiece, while an end mill (b) only has cutting edges on the periphery of its base, an arrangement which precludes drilling operations

language has two parts, the first of which permits the user to create the 'unbounded geometry' that he requires, that is, points, infinite straight lines and complete circles. He can then use the unbounded geometry as the basis for defining profiles, which are called 'K-curves' in GNC. These consist of line segments and arcs and are derived from the unbounded geometry by indicating a number of the unbounded features to be visited in order, and the relationship, such as tangencies, between them. Fillet radii can be added as attributes of a corner in the K-curve—they do not have to be specified explicitly. K-curves need not be closed as the program does not attempt any automatic recognition of pockets and islands. When a set of K-curves has been defined, the programmer uses the graphics cursor on a display to specify the tool

movements. (In early versions of GNC this was the only stage at which graphics were provided. Now that graphics devices are much cheaper a display is commonly used to verify the geometry definition phases.) GNC will produce offsets from the K-curves, which form the basis of the profiling cutter path. The area clearance cutter path, on the other hand, is input entirely freehand using the cursor. Things like cutter descents can be positioned where the programmer knows they will give no trouble.

The 2½D representation is essentially a utilitarian one and supports few facilities besides cutter path generation. However, it is well suited to this role, and is sometimes 'stretched' in order to fulfil it. For instance, it is possible, indeed common, to use conical milling cutters, called diesinking cutters (Figure 3.16), to machine a cutter path produced on a 2½D system when making dies and moulds, which must have a draft angle so that the component can be released after it is made. In this case the geometry described is very different from that actually machined. In some systems, 2½D representations have been extended to allow the notionally flat and parallel 'bottom' and 'top' surfaces inside the profiles to be tilted at angles. Unless a numerical control milling machine has the appropriate

Figure 3.16 A conical diesinking slot drill for producing dies and moulds with a draft angle

rotational axes these surfaces are cut approx-imately. It is likely that 2½D systems will remain popular, and will be further stretched, until more complex software can match their speed and ease of use.

Wire frames

The two- and two-and-a-half-dimensional schemes that we have just discussed have been used as the basis for self-contained suites of programs, like GNC. They have also been employed by draughting system manufacturers seeking to extend their systems beyond two dimensions and the production of drawings. The idea of the 2½D shape is a useful and workable one, but its limits are clear. In this section we shall examine a less restricted representation, which has its origin in compu-ter graphics work and which has also been used as an extension to draughting systems. We shall see that this increased flexibility is obtained at the expense of severe problems which, ultimately, limit the applicability of the 'draughting system approach' to CAE.

A direct, and enticingly simple, way to extend a draughting system into three dimen-sions is to allow line segments to be positioned in space, rather than just a plane. There is no logical problem at all in extending the sorts of data structure we discussed in Chapter 2 into three dimensions. Points are simply specified as three coordinates (x, y, z) rather than two (x, y). If line segments are all defined in terms of their endpoints, no further changes are necessary. Alternatively, the parametric line equation

$$x = x_0 + ft$$
$$y = y_0 + gt$$

can easily be extended into three dimensions:

$$x = x_0 + ft$$
$$y = y_0 + gt$$
$$z = z_0 + ht$$

The definition of a line segment, as a beginning and an end value of the parameter t, remains unchanged.

Arcs are more complicated in three dimen-sions, because the plane in which the arc lies must be defined. It may be fixed by the triangle formed by the arc's centre and endpoints, provided that these do not happen to be collinear. We might expect most arcs to lie in planes perpendicular to the coordinate axes, and it may well be efficient to treat these arcs as special cases, or even to restrict a program to deal only with arcs of this type. Whatever the details of an implementation, we end up with a lot of line segments positioned in space and joined to other line segments at their endpoints. We could make a physical model of this set-up by cutting up a few old wire coat-hangers and brazing their ends together. Structures of this sort are therefore referred to as *wire frame* models.

Pictures

The wire frame is the first fully three-dimensional shape representation that we have met. It raises an immediate problem: how are we going to depict it on a graphics screen or piece of paper that is only two-dimensional?

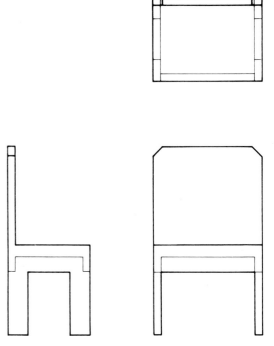

Figure 3.17 Three orthographic views of a wire frame of a chair. The thin lines in this hand-drawn picture are those which would not appear in an engineering drawing

We can easily produce three pictures by ignoring the *x*, *y* and *z* coordinates in turn. These three views will be similar to those that we might construct, one at a time, using a draughting system with only two-dimensional facilities. However, these pictures will not necessarily be views in the engineering drawing sense. In particular, edges from the far side of the component, which would not appear in an engineering drawing, may be visible (Figure 3.17). Such unwanted lines can be deleted interactively, and each view annotated with dimensions and an engineering drawing produced. One reason for creating a wire frame is indeed to take some of the work out of preparing a number of different views of a single component on a draughting system.

There are many ways of producing a picture from three-dimensional data that make visual sense. They are called *projections*. Just ignoring one of the coordinates is one way of achieving a *parallel* projection. A parallel projection of a wire frame can be considered as

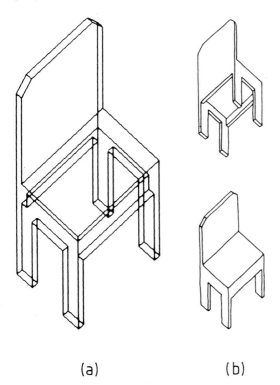

(a)   (b)

Figure 3.18 The wire frame of Figure 3.17 (a) in isometric projection. The two equally valid interpretations (b) have been sketched in by hand

its shadow when lit by a parallel beam of light. Many different parallel projections can be obtained by different choices of direction of this 'light beam'. The well-known *isometric* projection (Figure 3.18) is similar to a parallel projection in which the light beam makes an equal angle with all three coordinate axes: lines parallel to the axes appear with angles of 120 degrees between them. In an isometric projection, however, the lines retain their original lengths, rather than being foreshortened, and the isometric is thus not quite a true parallel projection. Many wire frames of objects of engineering interest consist principally of lines which are parallel to the coordinate axes, and for such shapes an isometric provides a way of displaying all the edges, without distorting their lengths, in a single view. If any great proportion of the 'wires' are not parallel to any of the axes, however, an isometric projection is merely confusing.

Figure 3.18 illustrates one of the problems with isometric projections, even when there are hardly any lines at funny angles. They give no sense of depth, and the picture appears to 'flip' between two possible interpretations: a view from above and a view from below. Removing the lines that would not appear in a picture of a solid object is one way to stop this happening. Even if we remove the unwanted lines by hand, the isometric projection still gives a distorted picture: the part of the object furthest from the viewer appears to be 'lifting up' towards him. To remedy this defect we must use a true *perspective* projection (Figure 3.19). This corresponds to the way a camera or an artist (Canaletto, say, not Picasso) records a three-dimensional scene on a two-dimensional medium. Objects further away from the viewer are made to shrink in relation to nearer ones. This is not very difficult to program on a computer. Suppose, looking at Figure 3.20, that we have decided on a viewpoint and a viewing direction. We now put an imaginary 'projection plane' between the viewpoint and the scene (the wire frame in this case) and perpendicular to the viewing direction. To find where each point in the scene appears on the projection plane we trace a straight line back from the point of interest in the scene to the viewpoint. Where that line crosses the projection plane is where that point appears in the

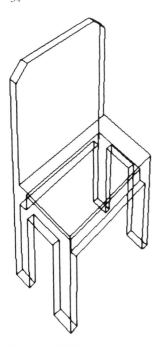

Figure 3.19 The wire frame of Figure 3.17 in perspective projection

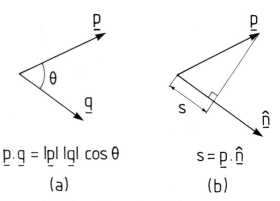

$$\underline{p}.\underline{q} = |\underline{p}| \, |\underline{q}| \cos \theta \qquad s = \underline{p}.\hat{\underline{n}}$$

$$(a) \qquad\qquad (b)$$

Figure 3.21 The scalar product (a) between two vectors p and q may be interpreted geometrically as shown. It can also be calculated from the components of the two vectors:

$$p \cdot q = x_p x_q + y_p y_q + z_p z_q$$

The projection (b) of a point onto an axis can be achieved by taking the scalar product of the vector to that point with a vector of unit length along the axis. (This figure is for readers who are already familiar with vectors. They will be introduced more gently in Chapter 4)

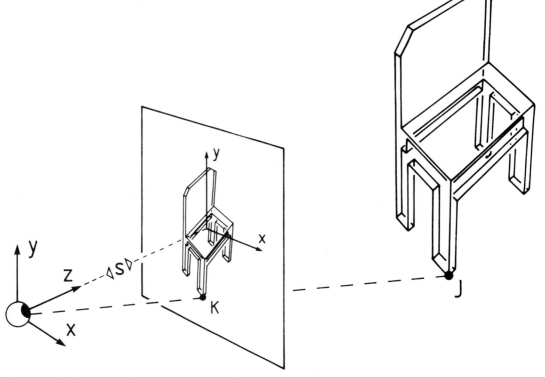

Figure 3.20 The mechanics of perspective projection. The viewpoint, which is also the coordinate origin, is drawn as an eyeball. (The other symbols are explained in the text)

picture. Doing this in the computer, we set up a new Cartesian coordinate system which has the viewpoint as origin, one coordinate axis (conventionally z) along the viewing direction and the other two axes parallel to the edges of the projection plane. To project a point onto the projection plane we first calculate its coordinates in the new system, by taking the *scalar product* (explained in Figure 3.21) of its original coordinates with each of the new axes in turn. If a point J has coordinates (x_J, y_J, z_J), referred to these new axes, then the corresponding projected point K will have coordinates $(sx_J/z_J, sy_J/z_J, s)$, where s is the distance from the viewpoint to the projection plane. The division by z_J produces the shrinking of objects further from the viewpoint that we associate with perspective. The z coordinate of the projected point K may be discarded, leaving its projected two-dimensional position as $(sx_J/z_J, sy_J/z_J)$, with respect to an origin at the centre of the projection plane.

Projections are required to display every sort of three-dimensional shape representation as a two-dimensional picture, not just wire frames. It has merely been convenient to deal with projections at their first occurrence. There are, however, a number of display possibilities that are peculiar to the wire frame, and the existence of these means that it is sometimes appropriate to transform more sophisticated shape models into wire frames if one of these types of display is required. The simplest such technique is called *haloing*.[2] There is insufficient information in a wire frame to permit the removal of entire lines that 'should be' invisible, but we do know which lines are in front of which others. If we display the picture with a gap in a line where another crosses in front of it, then the ambiguity of the wire frame is reduced. This technique has been in use for many years in drawing diagrams, by hand, for geometry textbooks. In some cases, where the object is not too complicated, the 'crystal' effect which haloing produces (Figure 3.22) may be preferable to the full removal of lines which should be hidden, because detail on both near and far sides of the object is visible simultaneously and in a single view.

An alternative way to indicate the relative distance from the viewer of various parts of a wire frame is to make the more distant parts of

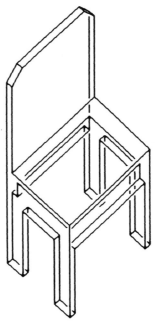

Figure 3.22 Haloing performed on the wire frame of Figure 3.17. The isometric projection is identical to that in Figure 3.18, but the ambiguity is eliminated

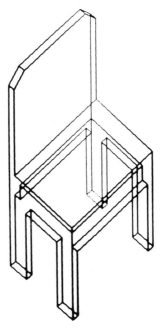

Figure 3.23 Depth cueing performed on the wire frame of Figure 3.17. The projection is the isometric of Figure 3.18, and the ambiguity is eliminated

the structure fainter than the nearer ones, as though the viewer were seeing the wire frame through a fog (Figure 3.23). It is called *depth cueing*, and requires a display that is capable of a number of different line intensities. Storage tubes cannot do this, so depth cueing is restricted to raster-scan and vector refresh display. A wide range of intensities is helpful, as these have to be spread out between the back and front of the object. If there are too few intensity levels, then pairs of lines which cross quite close to each other in depth may end up the same shade and ambiguity will creep back into the picture. Ultimately, even with the most sophisticated display, the efficiency of depth cueing is limited by the range of intensities that the human eye can distinguish.

Haloing and depth cueing are useful techniques, but the trump card in the display of wire frames is held by the vector refresh display. We have already mentioned how modifying entries in the display list can give fast deletion and the illusion of objects moving across the screen. The most sophisticated vector refresh displays can be loaded with a display list consisting of three-dimensional line segments and then programmed to calculate a new projection each time the list is processed. As the projection is changed, a wire frame may be made to appear to tumble and spin around the screen, and to move towards the viewer and away again. These gyrations can be programmed or controlled interactively from a joystick. The latter makes it possible to turn the wire frame to examine a feature of interest, and the motion itself gives a very good impression of the three-dimensional nature of the data.

In general, wire frames and the associated display techniques offer a quick and easy way to visualize relatively simple shapes. As shapes become more complex, the impossibility of fully removing hidden detail becomes a major disadvantage (Figure 3.24).

Limitations

The development of a number of draughting systems into wire frame systems was initially accompanied by claims to provide a 'full three-dimensional capability'. Programmers working for draughting system vendors made

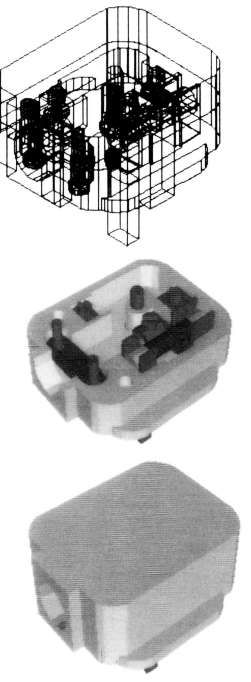

Figure 3.24 This wire frame (top), of a UK standard electric plug, is not particularly complicated but it is nevertheless difficult to make sense of the isometric view shown. 'Photographic' views of the same object (actually computed from a solid model) are immediately understandable, even though displayed at low resolution

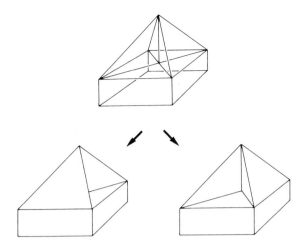

Figure 3.25 A wire frame with two distinct interpretations as a solid object

dimensions. Any partial success that these attempts enjoyed was the result of programmers introducing assumptions into their programs about typical engineering components, and of programs requesting a lot of help from their users. It is (now) easy to show that these efforts were fundamentally futile, simply by demonstrating that a single wire frame can quite legitimately represent the edges of two or more objects. Figure 3.25 presents a simple example. If the object that a wire frame represents is not unique, then it is clearly impossible to determine a single correct set of object properties from it. Since this has been fully realized, there have been a number of interesting programs written to associate objects with wire frames, written in the full knowledge of their ambiguity. Some (admittedly slightly bizarre) wire frames have been shown to correspond to literally thousands of possible objects.[46] It is clear that we must look for other shape representations if we wish to create genuine models of fully three-dimensional objects.

valiant efforts to write programs to do things like calculate volumes from wire frames, which were facilities (rightly) felt to be part of a fully three-dimensional system. After all, it is easy to calculate the area of a profile in two

4

Curves to curved surfaces

Many manufactured articles have surfaces which are more complex than those, such as planes and cylinders, which can readily be produced on conventional machine tools. It is difficult to draw them, and impossible using straight lines and circular arcs alone. A spectacle case, a telephone and a car body are examples within everyone's experience. Here are three reasons why an object may need to have a curved form:

(1) For the object to function correctly. The most common example of this is the requirement for fluid dynamic performance. Clearly both ships and aircraft would be spectacularly inefficient if they were not designed to this criterion.
(2) To meet aesthetic standards. This consideration is very important in many consumer goods, such as kitchen equipment and power tools.
(3) To facilitate manufacture. Many methods of making components in bulk, such as casting, forging and injection moulding, require a shape which does not have sharp corners. It may be appropriate to select such a process because a complex surface is required, or the surface forms may be incorporated in the design mainly to take advantage of the manufacturing method.

Where the form of a component is closely controlled by its function, as for instance with an aerofoil, then the shape definition is almost always directly linked to analytical or numerical information about that requirement. In many cases, however, neither functional nor

manufacturing considerations force the use of a particular shape definition: functional, manufacturing and aesthetic requirements are all present. A car body shell is a good example: it must contain the passengers and the other parts of the car satisfactorily, it should have a low drag coefficient, it must be manufactured using press tools at reasonable cost, and it must be attractive enough to sell. The designer has to juggle the shape intelligently to try to fulfil all these requirements.

It is not easy to construct shape elements that can be used by a designer in this task. Shape representations must be sought that are not only well behaved in the mathematical sense but which also behave predictably in response to actions by the user. He must quickly become aware of the effects he can achieve on shapes with the 'handles' provided by a representation. Also, the representation should not be too expensive to compute for any of the purposes for which it may be required. This chapter and Chapter 6 attempt to show some of the ways in which people have attempted to produce controllable shape elements for describing complex-surfaced objects. These techniques are well represented in the literature,[24,58] where more detail can be found. We will start simply in two dimensions by looking at complex curves.

Parametric curves

It is possible to create complex curves from multiple segments of the classical curves, usually circular or parabolic arcs. However, thee can only give limited continuity (differentiability) and the large numbers of segments required are not easy to organize and control. In general, it is more satisfactory to use fewer segments of more complex form. (The decision between many and simple or few and complex is central to the whole topic of curves and curved surfaces.)

The evaluation of all functions in the computer eventually reduces to the computation of *polynomials*—expressions of the form

$$a + bx + cx^2 + dx^3 \quad \ldots$$

and *rational polynomials*:

$$\frac{a + b_1x + c_1x^2 + d_1x^3 \quad \ldots}{a + b_2x + c_2x^2 + d_2x^3 \quad \ldots}$$

(Note that, for computational purposes, the form

$$a + x(b + x(c + x(d \quad \ldots \quad)))$$

considerably reduces the number of multiplications required to evaluate a polynomial.) It seems sensible to seek to extend known polynomial curve equations rather than to introduce other functions, such as, say, exponentials, which would in any case reduce to polynomials during computation. Generalizing the implicit circle equation gives the implicit equation of a general conic section:

$$ax^2 + by^2 + 2cxy + 2dx + 2ey + f = 0$$

The disadvantage of using implicit equations for generating more complex curves becomes immediately apparent: it is necessary to solve the equation in order to generate points on the curve. This can be done analytically with a quadratic but, if many more terms are added, only numerical solutions are possible.

This difficulty can be avoided by extending the parametric straight line equation

$$x = x_0 + ft$$
$$y = y_0 + gt$$

by adding higher order terms in t. We can construct (after changing notation) equations of the form:

$$x = a_1 + b_1t + c_1t^2 + d_1t^3 + \quad \ldots$$
$$y = a_2 + b_2t + c_2t^2 + d_2t^3 + \quad \ldots$$

With additional terms in t^2 only, the equation and hence, loosely, the curve, is called a quadratic. With t^3 added it becomes a cubic, and so on. (Rational parametric polynomials may also be used as curve equations, although this requires more attention to numerical problems. One advantage they have is that circular arcs can be represented exactly, using the circle parameterization given in Chapter 2. For simplicity, however, rational parametric curves are not mentioned again in this book.)

Writing separate equations in each of the two coordinates is rather repetitive, and so the form

$$\mathbf{Q}(t) = \mathbf{A} + \mathbf{B}t + \mathbf{C}t^2 + \mathbf{D}t^3 + \quad \ldots$$

is often used, where the coefficients in capitals are *vectors*, containing one number that relates to the equation for x, and one to the equation for y. The vector quantity $\mathbf{Q}(t)$ refers to the coordinates of a point on the curve: '(t)' indicates that a particular point can be obtained by substituting an actual value of t into the equations. (By considering its components as lengths rather than coordinates a vector may also be used to represent a combined length and direction unconnected with a particular point in space. This concept was used without introduction in describing the scalar product (Figure 3.21) and is important in the present context when we come to differentiate curves and surfaces. As the example of the scalar product shows, vector notation can be extended without difficulty into three dimensions.)

Using parametric polynomial equations does not lead directly to curves which are controllable. Consider a parametric quadratic, the simplest curve in this family:

$$\mathbf{Q}(t) = \mathbf{A} + \mathbf{B}t + \mathbf{C}t^2$$

or

$$x = a_1 + b_1t + c_1t^2$$
$$y = a_2 + b_2t + c_2t^2$$

Altering $\mathbf{A}$ (a_1 and a_2) will clearly change the distance of the curves from the axes, but the effect of changing the other coefficients is not easy to visualize. Direct alteration of the coefficients of parametric polynomials is useless as a means of controlling them.

Interpolation

One of the simplest ways to control a parametric polynomial curve is to constrain it to pass, or *interpolate*, through a number of points. For example, suppose that we want to make a quadratic pass through (x_1, y_1), (x_2, y_2) and (x_3, y_3) in that order. It is first necessary to decide what value the parameter will have as it passes through each point. (This can be one of the major headaches of parametric interpolation, as different curves result from different parameterizations of the points.) By convention, we make the segment of a parametric curve in which we are interested run from parameter value 0 to parameter value 1.

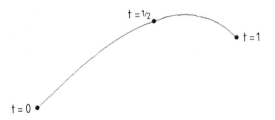

Figure 4.1 A parametric quadratic curve interpolating through three points

Suppose that, as shown in Figure 4.1, the three points are to correspond to parameter values 0, ½ and 1 respectively. We can set up two sets of simultaneous equations, one for each coordinate direction, by substituting in the x and y values at the points through which the curve must pass, and the corresponding values of t. In this particular case the equations in x give:

at (x_1, y_1) $t = 0$, therefore $x_1 = a_1$
at (x_2, y_2) $t = \frac{1}{2}$, therefore $x_2 = a_1 + \frac{1}{2}b_1 + \frac{1}{4}c_1$
at (x_3, y_3) $t = 1$, therefore $x_3 = a_1 + b_1 + c_1$

Solving for the three coefficients, we obtain:

$a_1 = x_1$
$b_1 = 4x_2 - 3x_1 - x_3$
$c_1 = 2x_1 - 4x_2 + 2x_3$

This form of interpolation, through data points, is called *Lagrangian* interpolation.

In most cases, however, a curve segment must have given slopes as well as positions at its ends (if not elsewhere) to allow it to mate with adjoining curves. Interpolation to both position and slope constraints is known as

Hermite interpolation. It can be achieved by differentiating the parametric polynomials with respect to t:

$$x = a_1 + b_1 t + c_1 t^2 + d_1 t^3 \quad + \quad \dots$$
$$y = a_2 + b_2 t + c_2 t^2 + d_2 t^3 \quad + \quad \dots$$

$$\frac{dx}{dt} = b_1 + 2c_1 t + 3d_1 t^2 + \dots$$

$$\frac{dy}{dt} = b_2 + 2c_2 t + 3d_2 t^2 + \dots$$

The resulting equations for dx/dt and dy/dt may be used to set up further simultaneous equations for the desired values of these quantities at given values of t. A further problem of parameterization is introduced here. A specified value of gradient dy/dx does not imply unique values of dx/dt and dy/dt: they may both be scaled by a factor. Large values of dx/dt and dy/dt 'stretch' the parameter along the curve and take the slope constraint deeper into the curve (Figure 4.2).

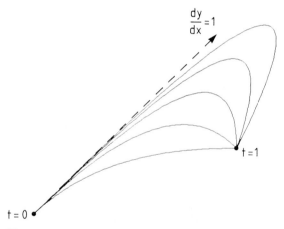

Figure 4.2 A parametric quadratic curve interpolating between two points with a slope constraint at the first point. The gradient specified (dy/dx) is constant as 1, but the values of both dx/dt and dy/dt are 2, 4, 6, 8 and 10 in successive curves (from bottom to top)

Satisfying each slope constraint requires one more term to be added to the equations in each of x and y. For this reason the cubic, which has four terms and can therefore satisfy both position and slope constraints at its ends, is the lowest order parametric polynomial commonly used (Figure 4.3):

$$\mathbf{Q}(t) = \mathbf{A} + \mathbf{B}t + \mathbf{C}t^2 + \mathbf{D}t^3$$

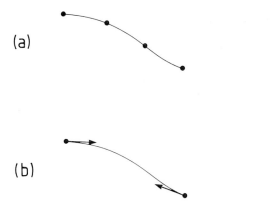

(a)

(b)

Figure 4.3 A parametric cubic can be specified by (a) Lagrangian interpolation between four position constraints, or (b) Hermite interpolation between two position and two slope constraints. Note that in (b) both arrows point 'into' the curve. This is a diagrammatic convention indicating that the slope constraints belong to this curve segment. If the arrows represented actual values of dx/dt and dy/dt, the direction of one arrow would be reversed (which one depending on the direction of parameterization)

or

$$x = a_1 + b_1 t + c_1 t^2 + d_1 t^3$$
$$y = a_2 + b_2 t + c_2 t^2 + d_2 t^3$$

This is not the end of the story. There is often a requirement for curves with more flexibility than parametric cubic permits. If such curves are generated by specifying many intermediate data points then the problem of choosing appropriate parameter values becomes acute. Wrong choices lead to 'wiggles' (Figure 4.4) between the data points which may be very difficult to eliminate. Chord length, the distance between successive data points, may be used to generate the parameter values, as in POLYSURF,[26] but even this is not always satisfactory. Furthermore, there may be numerical difficulties in solving the

Figure 4.4 'Wiggles' in a high-order parametric curve caused by wrong choices of parameter values at the points to which it is interpolated. The dotted line is a notional 'fair' curve

large sets of simultaneous equations that are generated, and this can be time-consuming on small computers.

Bézier curves

There are other approaches to interpolation, one of which is the *Bézier curve*.[6,29] This is a method of formulating a parametric polynomial to meet the constraints of a designer's conceptions, rather than the rigid specification of interpolation. The technique is based on the input of a series of points, which may be joined to form a 'track'. The resulting curve starts at the first point of the track and finishes at the last one. Additionally, the curve starts and finishes with the gradients of the first and last track lines respectively. Otherwise, the intermediate points only *influence* the curve: it does not pass through them. However, the resulting curve is guaranteed to be 'smoother' than its track (Bézier curves are said to have a *variation diminishing* property) and so things cannot get out of hand as they can with interpolation.

To generate a Bézier curve we start with a track of $m + 1$ points $\mathbf{P}_{i(i=0,m)}$ (each $\mathbf{P}$ is a vector quantity and comprises terms for both the x and y coordinates of the point). The curve $\mathbf{Q}(t)$ is then given by:

$$\mathbf{Q}(t) = \sum_{i=0}^{i=m} \frac{m!}{(m-i)!i!} \, t^i (1-t)^{m-i} \mathbf{P}_i$$

($m!$, or m *factorial*, is the product of m with all the positive integers smaller than itself. For instance $5! = 5 \times 4 \times 3 \times 2 \times 1 = 120$. Note that $0!$ is defined to be 1, *not* 0.) The effect of this rather daunting equation is to generate a curve by adding together proportions of the point data which vary with the parameter t, thus changing the extent to which each track point influences the curve. We can consider each term

$$\frac{m!}{(m-i)!i!} \, t^i (1-t)^{m-i}$$

of the curve equation as a *weighting function* applied to the ith track point (remember that i starts at 0). Figure 4.5 shows these weighting functions for a Bézier curve with four track points, which is therefore a cubic. The functions' behaviour at $t = 0$ and $t = 1$ shows

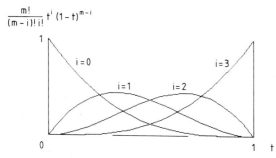

$$\frac{m!}{(m-i)!\,i!}\,t^{i}\,(1-t)^{m-i}$$

Figure 4.5 The weighting functions corresponding to a cubic Bézier curve ($m = 3$)

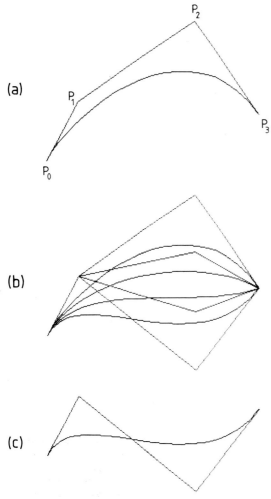

Figure 4.6 A cubic Bézier curve (a) between four track points which are labelled to correspond with the Bézier curve equation. Moving the third track point P_2 gives (b) a controlled sequence of changes resulting (c) in a new curve

how the merger of curve and track is achieved at the ends of the span. At each end only the corresponding end track point has any weight, which achieves the positional constraint. Of the other track points, only the weighting function of the next adjacent track point leaves the end with anything other than zero slope, and this produces the tangency of track and curve. (These observations can be substantiated by substituting $t = 0$ and $t = 1$ into the curve equation, before and after differentiating with respect to t.) Note that the equation is arranged so that the weights add up to 1 at any point, which preserves the curve's independence from the coordinate axes.

An example cubic curve corresponding to four particular vertices is shown in Figure 4.6. The figure also shows the effect of moving one of the middle track points. This is as far as we can get on paper towards demonstrating the intuitive understanding of the behaviour of Bézier curves that it is possible to achieve. Sitting at a display, it is easy to learn to anticipate the changes that must be made to the track of a particular Bézier curve to achieve a desired effect. Bézier curves have been used extensively at Renault, where they were developed. Their success supports the idea that, for interactive work, the exact mechanism that controls a shape is not so important, as long as the control is predictable and easy to use.

Composite curves

If a long curve is to be designed, perhaps where some portion must fulfil precise conditions while others may be specified with more of a 'broad brush', then it is usually best to join more than one curve segment together. Such composite curves are often called *splines*.[1] They have this name because of the similarity of the approach to the physical spline, a flexible lath which acts as a template for drawing smooth curves. This is used by fixing its position at intervals, using weights called 'ducks', but otherwise allowing it to spring into a smooth shape.

The supports in the physical system correspond to the joints between the curve segments, which are called *knots* (Figure 4.7). It can be shown that the slope of a physical spline is

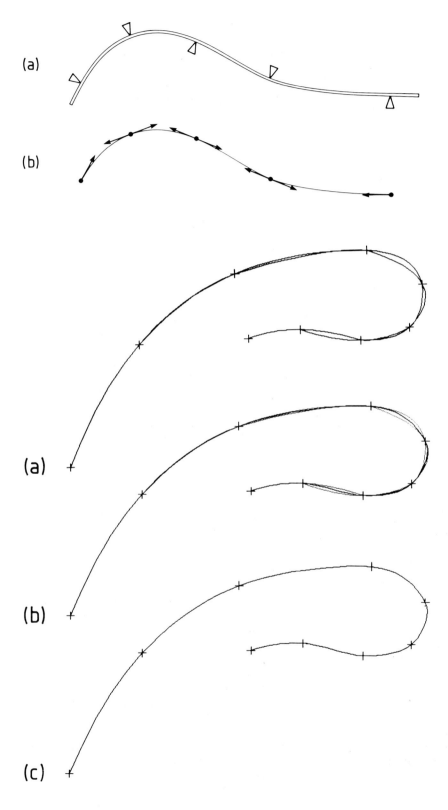

(a)

(b)

Figure 4.7 (a) A draughtsman's spline and (b) a spline curve made up of parametric cubic curve segments. (While the comparison is valuable, note that a spline curve in this form is *not* an exact analogue of the physical system)

(a)

(b)

(c)

Figure 4.8 An Overhauser curve is created by (a) linking the points to be interpolated in threes by parametric quadratics. These segments are combined (b) using a blending function which produces (c) a smooth curve

continuous and, further, so is the derivative of slope. The simplest curve that allows this behaviour to be imitated is the cubic parametric polynomial. It was shown earlier that cubics will normally only fulfil position and slope constraints at their ends. However, in the cubic spline, only the positional constraints are specified at the knots between the curves. Adjacent spans 'share' slope and second-order conditions at the knots: they must be the same but are not constrained to any particular value. For the whole spline, the number of constraints in each dimension is two fewer than the number of available coefficients, taking all the cubics together. These remaining constraints are usually supplied as end conditions and the whole system is solved as a set of simultaneous equations. Only then can the actual slopes and second derivatives at the knots be determined. Once these values are available, points on the resulting cubics are much quicker to compute than points on a single high-order curve, and the cubic spline is less prone to wiggles. Additionally, although moving one of the initial data points alters the whole spline, the effect is lessened along the curve: the cubic spline's behaviour is said to be *damped*.

A second, less common but engagingly simple, approach to composite curves is the *Overhauser curve*.[51] The series of points through which a long curve is required are first joined in sets of three by short curves, using Lagrangian interpolation. (Overhauser used implicit quadratics (parabolas) for this but it is possible to implement a similar parametric scheme.) Across each span a third, resultant, curve is obtained from the two 'alternative versions' by applying a blending function (Figure 4.8). This blending is arranged so that the contribution of each short curve (except the first and last) is zero at its start and end, and unity at the middle one of the three points it links. A linear blending function achieves slope continuity along the final curve, and this is what Overhauser used. (In this case each span is in fact a parametric cubic: the Overhauser formulation simply provides a good way of choosing tangents at the data points.) More complex versions of the same system will give higher order continuity. This form of curve is well behaved and economical to compute. A major advantage for many applications is that a change to a single data point only affects the rest of the curve for two segments either way, not along its whole length.

B-spline curves

The *B-spline*[33] is a relatively recent generalization of the Bézier curve that promises to make a considerable contribution to CAE systems. Its popularity can be attributed to the fact that it combines the controllability of the Bézier curve with the stability over long spans exhibited by the composite curves that we have just discussed. The idea behind the B-spline is most easily grasped if we consider the weights applied to the track points in the Bézier formulation. Every track point has some influence over every point on the curve (except at the extreme ends). With a lot of track points, the requirement to fulfil so many constraints means using an equation of undesirably high order, and changes made to a track point have a less precise and localized effect than we might desire. The B-spline is based on the same kind of track as the Bézier curve, but the effect of each track point is limited to a proportion of the span. The reduced number of constraints to be met at any point also gives a lower order equation, but of course one which changes from the vicinity of one control point to another.

How are these changes of equation handled in the B-spline? Unlike conventional splines, it is not a matter of determining the end derivatives of spans of which the end points are already specified. Instead, both the positions and derivatives are obtained from a single formulation, which itself incorporates discontinuities that allow separate spans to be generated. B-spline polynomials are mathematical expressions that can be defined *recursively*, meaning 'in terms of themselves'. This makes B-splines rather hard to understand, but easy to program, especially in a computer language which permits subprograms to call themselves. The equation of a B-spline of order k is:

$$\mathbf{Q}(t) = \sum_{i=0}^{i=m} B_{i,k}(t)\mathbf{P}_i$$

Like the Bézier formulation, $\mathbf{P}_{i(i=0,m+k)}$ is the set of track point coordinate vectors, and $\mathbf{Q}(t)$ is the curve. $B_{i,k}(t)$ is a B-spline polynomial of order k which is defined as follows:

$$B_{i,k}(t) = \frac{t - T_i}{T_{i+k-1} - T_i} B_{i,k-1}(t)$$
$$+ \frac{T_{i+k} - t}{T_{i+k} - T_{i+1}} B_{i+1,k-1}(t)$$

In other words it is defined in terms of two further B-spline polynomials of order $k - 1$. This process of recursion must stop somewhere, and in fact the first-order B-spline polynomial is defined differently:

$$B_{i,1}(t) = 1 \quad \text{if } T_i \leqslant t \leqslant T_{i+1}$$
$$= 0 \quad \text{otherwise}$$

which is where the discontinuities come into the formulation. Finally, we need to explain the symbols $T_{i(i=0,m+k)}$. These refer to a set of parameter *values* that define where the joints in the curve occur. Using the same nomenclature as for ordinary splines, they are called knots, and the whole $m + k + 1$ of them is called the *knot vector*. The knots must be in ascending numerical order ($T_1 \leqslant T_{i+1}$), but otherwise can have any values. Integer knots are commonly used to keep things simple. (Readers who have found the algebra of the B-spline definition puzzling may like to know that Rogers and Adams[58] give a complete worked example.)

Figure 4.9 shows the weighting functions produced by B-spline polynomials of order 2, 3, 4 and 5 (values of k). At order 2 the corresponding curve segments are actually the lines of the track. (The curve of order 1 corresponds to the track *points* only!) As the order gets higher the curve segments become quadratic, cubic and then quartic. The curve becomes smoother in the mathematical sense (it has higher order continuity), but the effect of each track point extends to a longer and longer portion of the curve, which follows the track less closely. Figure 4.9 shows what the weighting functions look like in the middle of a long curve. In order to use a B-spline we would like its ends to meet the end track points, and to start and finish tangential to the first and last sides of the track, like a Bézier curve. These properties can be achieved by repeating a number of knots equal to the order of the curve

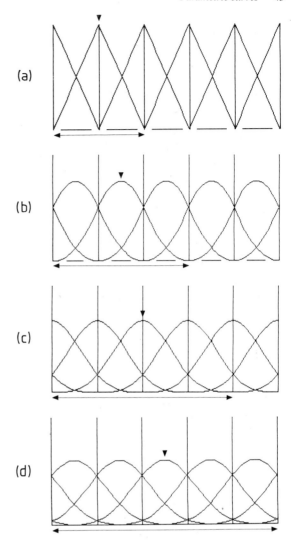

(a)

(b)

(c)

(d)

Figure 4.9 Weighting functions generated by B-spline polynomials of (a) order 2 (linear), (b) order 3 (quadratic), (c) order 4 (cubic) and (d) order 5 (quartic), all with equally spaced knots. The arrowed lines show the way in which the parametric length of a single polynomial increases, corresponding to a track point influencing a longer portion of a curve

at the beginning and end of the knot vector. Figure 4.10 shows how a third order (quadratic) B-spline with five vertices can be made to behave in this way by specifying the knots as (t =) 0, 0, 0, 1, 2, 3, 3 and 3 (written 00012333). A cubic B-spline with the knot vector 000012222 fulfils the same conditions and makes a smoother curve, but the influence of

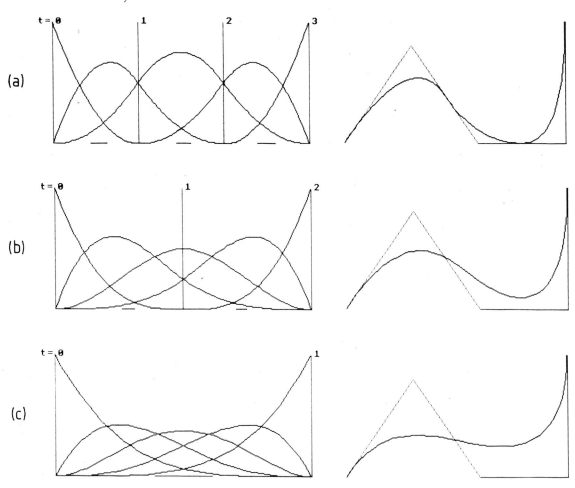

Figure 4.10 A track of five points used to generate B-splines of (a) order 3 (quadratic), (b) order 4 (cubic) and (c) order 5 (quartic), which corresponds to a Bézier curve. (The knot vectors used to generate these curves are mentioned in the text)

each track point is less concentrated. Finally, look at the quartic curve in Figure 4.10, which has the knot vector 0000011111. In this case there are no intermediate knots and each track point has an effect along the entire curve and, yes, this *is* a Bézier curve! The B-spline definition tidily takes in Bézier as this extreme case. Note the way in which both the number of knots and the resulting parametric length of the curve increase with the order of the spline.

The B-spline is most commonly used in the way we have just seen, with n knots of value zero at the beginning of the knot vector, k knots of value $m - k$ at the end, and the middle knots consisting of the first $m - k + 1$

integers. It is also possible to introduce *repeated knots* into the middle of the curve. This gives a closer approximation to the track but also produces a local reduction of the curve's continuity. The effect of a repeated knot occurs at a given parametric position on the curve and may not be easy to relate to the positions of the track points. A more useful way of gaining extra control is to repeat one or more track points. (This can be done with Bézier curves too, but with Bézier curves more points necessitate an increase in the order of the curve.) A *repeated track point* pulls the curve very sharply towards that point, while not reducing its (mathematical) smoothness.

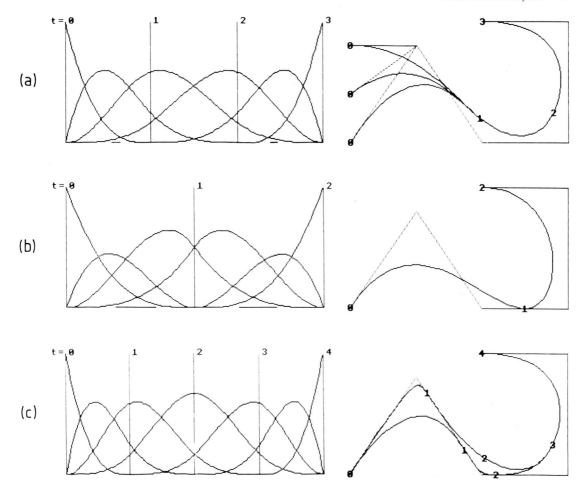

Figure 4.11 A track of six points is used (a) to generate a third-order (cubic) B-spline, with the knot vector 0000123333. The first track point has been moved to show how it only affects a parametrically limited portion of the curve. The knot vector 0000112222 introduces a repeated knot into the middle of the span, which (b) causes the curve to behave like a second-order (quadratic) B-spline in the centre of the span, at $t = 2$. Alternatively, (c) repeating the second or third track point generates changes that are easier to relate to the track. These last curves both have a longer knot vector (00001234444) to accommodate the extra track point. Note that beyond $t = 3$ this curve is the same as in (a). (The numbers superimposed on the curves are values of the parameter t)

Figure 4.11 shows an extended version of the curve of Figure 4.10, and the effect of repeating a knot and a track point.

If some consecutive track points are much closer than others they will have an effect very like a single repeated track point, and this may be undesirable. Non-integer knots are some-times chosen to compensate: the knot values can be based on the lengths of the track lines. Finally, it is worth stating that it is easy to use B-splines to generate closed curves, and that it is also possible to interpolate between points *on* the curve instead of, or as well as, track points,[49] although this reintroduces the need to solve sets of simultaneous equations.

Cross-sectional surfaces

By themselves, the complex curves we have just discussed are not very useful. Draughting systems usually have one or two complex curve types available. These can be used to approximate features such as intersection curves, or accurately to define flat objects with complex profiles, sometimes called tabulated cylinders or *tabcyls*, although there are not many such shapes of engineering interest. The ones that spring to mind are cams of various sorts. These are always shaped strictly from functional requirements: the velocity and acceleration that are to be imparted to the cam follower. Shape variations of a few hundredths of a millimetre can cause unacceptable vibration in mechanisms driven by high-speed cams. There is little scope for interactive, aesthetic, design of cams using, say, Bézier curves!

A tabcyl has a constant profile: that is why it can be defined by a single curve in a plane (and its thickness, of course). Suppose that an object is defined by a curve which changes its shape across the thickness of the object. This changing curve will define a surface which is no longer a simple cam-like shape: it is genuinely complex, curving both along and perpendicular to the plane of the original curve. We call this a *cross-sectional surface*—a surface specified in terms of its cross-sections.

The idea of cross-sectional surfaces is not a new one. It is the way in which ships and, latterly, aircraft have usually been specified. However, when such cross-sections are prepared manually there are some problems. Only a limited number of setions can be drawn, corresponding, say, to the ribs of a ship. The shape between the sections must be approximated, or interpolated, from them. It is rather like designing a landscape by specifying a contour map. As well as more information being needed to complete the design, it is not necessarily true that the cross-sections specified will be consistent with the overall smoothness, or *fairness*, of the shape. Suppose that we were making a timber boat in this way. We might find that, having made the ribs, the planking did not bend very naturally to fit them, producing bumps and hollows. This was for years a real problem in the shipbuilding industry. Templates were cut out in the shape of the ribs and laid out in the positions they would occupy in the hull. Thin strips of wood were then nailed onto those templates, in the longitudinal direction. If any unwanted bumps or hollows appeared, the shapes of the ribs

could be altered at this stage, rather than later and very expensively. As one might imagine, this process took up quite a lot of space. It was done, therefore, in the lofts of the shipyard buildings, and has come to be known as *lofting*. Ships and aircraft are still often spoken of as lofted shapes.

With a numerical shape definition there is no ambiguity about the profile at any position. This is achieved by making the curve definition dependent on the position of the plane in which it is defined: the distance along the hull, to return to our marine example. For instance, a parametric quadratic

$$x = a_1 + b_1 t + c_1 t^2$$
$$y = a_2 + b_2 t + c_2 t^2$$

might be rewritten:

$$x = (a_1 + a_1'z) + (b_1 + b_1'z)t + (c_1 + c_1'z)t^2$$
$$y = (a_2 + a_2'z) + (b_2 + b_2'z)t + (c_2 + c_2'z)t^2$$

For every value of z, a different parametric quadratic in the x and y plane is defined. We may consider this surface (Figure 4.12) as an

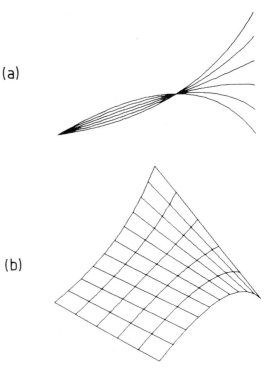

(a)

(b)

Figure 4.12 A linear transition (a) between two quadratic curves can be interpreted as (b) a ruled surface, seen here in isometric projection

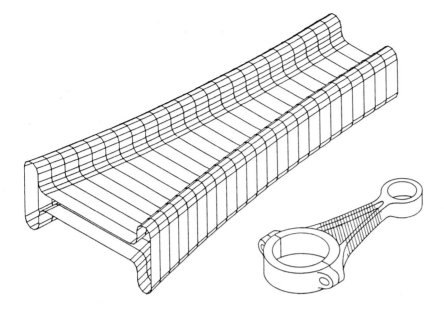

Figure 4.13 A surface defined as a cubic interpolation between cross-sections made up of line segments and arcs. As the inset shows, it is part of a connecting rod from an engine

interpolation, linear in this case, between the original curve, at $z = 0$, and the curve

$$x = (a_1 + a_1') + (b_1 + b_1')t + (c_1 + c_1')t^2$$
$$y = (a_2 + a_2') + (b_2 + b_2')t + (c_2 + c_2')t^2$$

at $z = 1$. (The coefficients of these end curves could be obtained by interpolation or by using the Bézier formulation.) Linear interpolation between cross-sections creates what are called *ruled* surfaces. They are of limited application, because it is normally necessary to make a smooth transition to adjoining surfaces at the defining cross-sections, for which a higher-order interpolation is required.

Just as the parametric cubic curve is able to satisfy both positional and slope constraints at its ends, a cubic interpolation between two cross-sections allows us to specify the way in which the interpolated surface meets each of them. Figure 4.13 shows a cross-sectional surface defined as just such a cubic interpolation between two closed cross-sections. In this case, however, the cross-sections themselves are not parametric polynomials but profiles constructed from line segments and arcs, defined by the 'elastic band' technique of the last chapter. Here a separate interpolating cubic is used to determine the centre and radius of each circle on the intermediate cross-sections. At one end (the far end in the figure) the shape becomes one of locally constant cross-section, but at the other end there is a marked expansion or *flare*. The individual control of the different parts of the profile has been used to give much more flare horizontally than vertically.

Ducts

So far we have assumed that the cross-sections comprising a cross-sectional surface are arranged on a series of parallel planes. It is quite feasible to relax this condition and gain a large increase in the range of shapes that can be represented. A convenient way to organize the successive planes, if they are not to be parallel, is to constrain them to be perpendicular to a single space curve. By *space curve* we mean a complex curve that does not lie in a plane. A space curve can be constructed from flat curve segments, such as arcs, lying in different planes but joined end to end. Alternatively we may extend the parametric curve equations that we have already examined to three dimensions. For instance, a parametric cubic space curve has the equations:

$$x = a_1 + b_1 t + c_1 t^2 + d_1 t^3$$
$$y = a_2 + b_2 t + c_2 t^2 + d_2 t^3$$
$$z = a_3 + b_3 t + c_3 t^2 + d_3 t^3$$

By making them perpendicular to a space curve we define the planes in which the

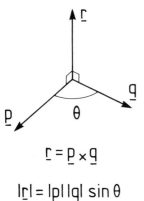

$$\underline{r} = \underline{p} \times \underline{q}$$

$$|\underline{r}| = |\underline{p}|\,|\underline{q}|\,\sin\theta$$

Figure 4.14 The vector product between two vectors *p* and *q* may be interpreted geometrically as shown. The components of the new vector *t* can also be calculated from the components of *p* and *q*:

$$x_r = y_p z_q - y_q z_p$$
$$y_r = z_p x_q - z_q x_p$$
$$z_r = x_p y_q - x_q y_p$$

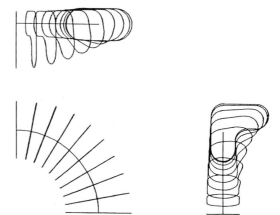

Figure 4.15 Three orthographic views of a duct constructed from cross-sections hung on a 'backbone' which is a cubic space curve. As in Figure 4.13, the cross-sections are profiles made from line segments and arcs

cross-sections are to lie in a continuous way, and also provide a natural conceptual handle on the definition. The space curve, which may be considered as a 'backbone', generates a unique set of cross-section planes (although the reverse is not true). Further information is needed, however, in addition to the backbone, to define the orientation of each cross-section on its plane. A unique vector in each plane can be obtained from the *vector product* (explained in Figure 4.14) of the gradient of the backbone and a suitable coordinate axis, although this is not foolproof.

Ducts can be used to describe engineering components, such as nozzles and elbows, for which the word duct would normally be used in any case. The cross-sections of the simplest such components may adequately be described by circles. The backbone might itself be a single circular arc. Figure 4.15 shows a shape almost as simple as this. Much more complicated components can be attempted, however, and these may retain a duct function, such as valve cavities or impeller casings (Figure 4.16). Less obviously, consumer items such as bottles and spectacle cases have been found to fit into the definition without difficulty. It is not necessary for the cross-sections to be closed

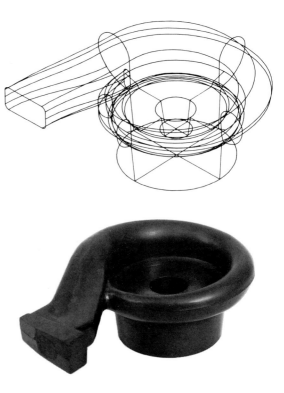

Figure 4.16 A duct defining the volute for a pump casing cavity displayed (top) as a wire frame. The resulting component is a core for casting. (The base of this object was also defined as a duct.) (Delta Computer Aided Engineering Ltd)

curves, and sheet metal components which are only semi-tubular can thus be modelled.

As well as the problem of orientating cross-sections, a difficulty arising when we abandon parallel cross-section planes is that one degree higher order continuity is required in the backbone than we wish to obtain on the surface of the duct, unless its cross-section is constant. In particular, a combination of arcs and line segments is less useful for constructing a backbone than we might have expected. This construction would be a natural choice for the engineer, but the fact that there can only be continuity of first derivative at the joints between arcs and line segments means that only positional continuity of the duct surface can be assured, unless it is of constant cross-section (Figure 4.17). Intuitively more obvious problems occur with a backbone that is not continuous in slope, and with large cross-sections hung onto a backbone with too small a radius of curvature (Figure 4.18).

The only large scale implementation of the duct representation is the eponymous DUCT system.[34,40] The space curves and cross-sections in the current version of this system are all defined in terms of cubic Bézier curve segments. A number of key cross-sections are created by the user, who also specifies the flare

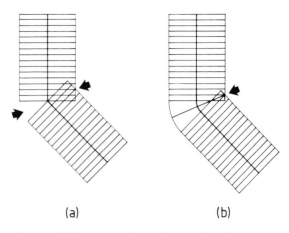

(a)   (b)

Figure 4.18 Portions of ducts (arrowed) which are nonsense from an engineering point of view can be constructed (a) by using a discontinuous backbone or (b) by hanging large cross-sections on a backbone with too small a radius of curvature, although in this case the surface is still algebraically continuous

of the duct at each segment of each cross-section. The logically rectangular areas of surface which are created are very nearly the patches that we shall deal with in Chapter 6, except that the lines of constant parameter running around the duct are constrained to be in a single plane. The use of cubics means that discontinuities in surface slope cannot be entirely avoided, but the DUCT system has an adjustment mechanism to keep them down to small values. These approximations are justified as being smaller than the inaccuracies that will necessarily occur in manufacture, particularly hand finishing. For many components, such as dies and patterns for casting and forging, this attitude seems reasonable if it can avoid unnecessary system complexity.

Intersections and blends

We shall see in Chapter 6 that, in general, calculating curves of intersection between surfaces is a complicated problem, and susceptible only to numerical solution. *Blends* are intersections made smooth by the introduction of a small radius or transition between the surfaces in question. A blend involves complicated algebra and also the introduction of a new piece of surface, which often needs to be

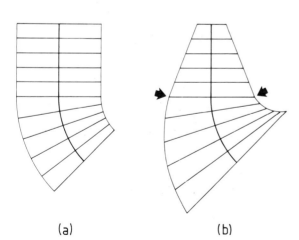

(a)   (b)

Figure 4.17 A continuous joint between an arc and a line in the 'backbone' of a duct produces (a) a smooth duct only if its cross-section is constant. If the duct is flared (b), the changing cross-sections lead to creases (arrowed) at positions corresponding to the joint in the backbone

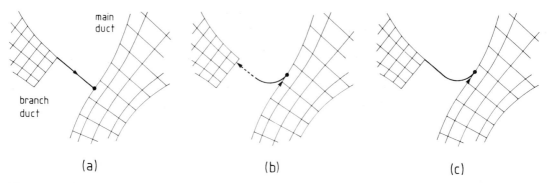

(a)   (b)   (c)

Figure 4.19 A numerical procedure to generate a blend between two ducts selects a number of points around the branch duct, and (a) extends straight lines from these onto the main duct. An iteration process (b) follows, which finishes when (c) a point on the main duct is found from which a connection to the branch duct with the appropriate radius can be made

of a different formulation to the surfaces that it joins in order to do its job.

As a surface type the duct is subject to these algebraic problems, but the DUCT package incorporates an approximate intersection and blending facility for making branching ducts. The technique is not universal in application, and in particular complex blend areas between three or more ducts must be avoided. We start with a 'main' duct, and also a 'branch' duct, which must terminate clear of the main duct's surface. The blending procedure selects a number of points around the circumference of the end of the branch duct and creates curves to the main duct from each of these in turn, using an iterative method illustrated in Figure 4.19. First, a straight line is drawn from each point in a direction corresponding to the slope along the branch duct. The program calculates where this strikes the main duct. If an intersection is all that is required, the operation is repeated for all the points around the end of the branch duct. If, on the other hand, we wish to make a blend, a new point on the main duct is chosen, from which, it is hoped, something nearer the desired blend curve can be calculated. This process of iteration terminates when a point on the main duct is found

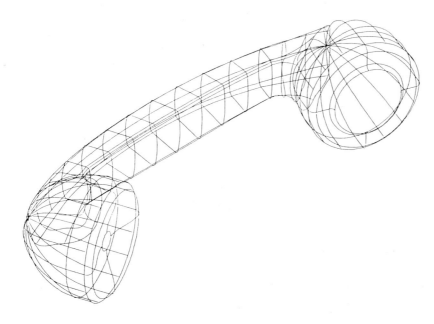

Figure 4.20 A telephone handset modelled as three ducts blended together and shown here as a wire frame. (Further pictures of this object produced using more sophisticated techniques appear in Figure 5.18.) (Delta Computer Aided Engineering Ltd)

from which a sufficiently accurate blend curve to the branch duct can be constructed. The blend curves that are created in these ways are assembled into a new duct. Of course, between the blend curves, it cannot be guaranteed that the blend duct will meet the main duct exactly. However, the match may be sufficiently close to enable the blend to be machined quite adequately. Figure 4.20 shows a telephone handset that incorporates two blends.

Applications

Having completed the design of a cross-sectional surface, whether defined on parallel planes or a duct, there are three ways in which we may use it. We can draw it, calculate various geometrical properties, or machine it. The possible ways of drawing these shapes are essentially those available for other sculptured surfaces. In particular, we may approximate the surface by a number of small pieces of flat surface and use the display techniques mentioned in the next chapter. Figures 5.6 and 5.18 are the ducts of Figures 4.15 and 4.20 respectively which have been displayed in this way. Such sophistication is often unnecessary in displaying simple cross-sectional surfaces defined on parallel planes. A view perpendicular to the planes of definition produces a contour map, something we have to go to some lengths to get with more complex surfaces. Almost all the information about the design is encapsulated in this one view, even though we may still want to obtain other pictures, for instance to judge 'fairness'.

Surface areas and surface moments are easily calculated from cross-sectional surfaces. Volume properties are less readily accessible, because in general the cross-sections are not the entire surface of the object. If the user can supply the missing geometry, volumes and volume properties can be calculated. This may be a simple matter, such as the case of a single closed duct, where we may write a program which assumes flat end caps. If the cross-sections are open, the user may well have to write a special program for each calculation that includes the geometry additional to the cross-sectional definition.

In machining, the difficulties are those which will be mentioned in detail in Chapter 6.

However, one particular problem that is common with (but not exclusive to) cross-sectional surfaces is cutter access. Unless a closed cross-sectional surface is a flat cone it cannot normally be machined with the cutter approaching the work from only a single direction. If the NC machine tool on which it is being cut has only the usual three axes, the cutter path must be segmented into at least two parts. These are then machined in successive set-ups, in each of which the workpiece is clamped in a different orientation to the cutter. The parts of the surface to be machined in each set-up can be determined from vectors perpendicular, or *normal*, to the surface. (The calculation of surface normals is dealt with in Chapter 6.) For a given orientation of the workpiece, parts of the surface with normals which point 'up' can be machined, parts with normals pointing 'down' cannot. (This of course ignores more complicated cases where cutter access is prevented by other parts of the component.) Sometimes this division into two parts has a significance beyond the machining strategy. If a cross-sectional surface is to be manufactured by die-casting or injection moulding, then the same technique of examining surface normals can be used to determine which part of the surface should be in the top half of the mould and how much in the bottom (Figure 4.21). The line between these two areas is called the split-line, and will in general be of arbitrary shape. This implies a curved surface where the two halves of the die or mould meet, like the one shown in Figure 4.22. This makes an interesting picture, but it is better to design components so that a flat split surface can be achieved.

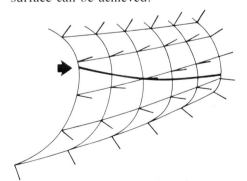

Figure 4.21 The split line (arrowed) on the side of a duct can be determined from the surface normals

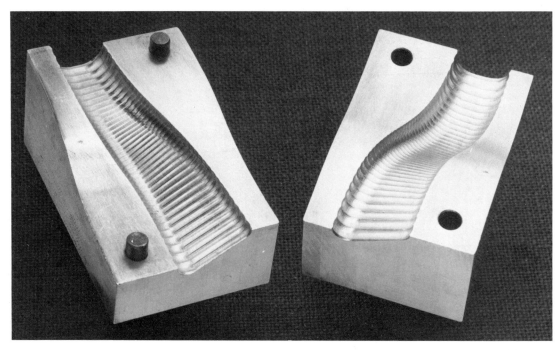

Figure 4.22 Two halves of a die made from a single duct definition, with a non-planar split surface (actually two tabcyls). The split surface has been hand finished, while the duct retains machining marks for illustrative purposes

5

Face models

The techniques covered so far were mainly developed by engineers with manufacture uppermost in their minds. At the same time, a number of people interested specifically in computer *graphics* (at the University of Utah in particular) were pursuing ways of producing realistic pictures of objects that they had no intention of making, or even of objects that would be impossible to make. (In the latter case, the word 'realistic' needs to be interpreted with some latitude.) The subject of 'pure' computer graphics is dealt with in detail by Newman and Sproull[47] and Foley and Van Dam.[27] This chapter discusses graphics techniques firstly because, as the representations used by engineers have become more sophisticated, more advanced ways of generating pictures have become necessary in communicating shape information. However, complete realism is not usually the goal in CAE. A second, better, reason for looking at this computer graphics work is to examine the face models on which it is largely based. We shall first describe these face models and then look at the processes by which pictures are produced from them.

A face model is essentially simple. It consists, as shown in Figure 5.1, of a list of pieces of surface of specified shape and position in space. In computer graphics work, flat faces have been used almost exclusively, in order to keep algorithms simple and fast. (As we shall see, this does not preclude the generation of pictures which give the impression that curved surfaces are being modelled.) Both the shape and position of the flat faces can be specified by listing the corners, or *vertices*, of each face. Vertex lists may be of

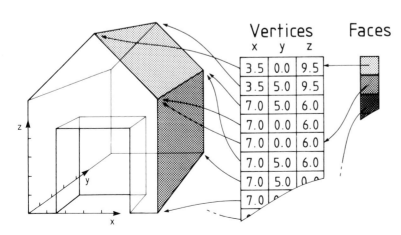

Vertices			Faces
x	y	z	
3.5	0.0	9.5	
3.5	5.0	9.5	
7.0	5.0	6.0	
7.0	0.0	6.0	
7.0	0.0	6.0	
7.0	5.0	6.0	
7.0	5.0	0.0	
7.0			

Figure 5.1 A simple data structure for a face model, in which each face record points into a list of vertices. The simple model shown here requires 11 face records and 18 vertex records, of which only a few have been shown

arbitrary length and the corresponding faces will then be polygons with any number of edges. One problem with the general polygon as a shape element is that we must trust the model creation process to put only coplanar points on each vertex list, otherwise a polygon is not part of a flat surface at all. Some display algorithms have been written to be tolerant of small deviations in this respect and permit some flexibility in 'polygon' creation. This is a blatant example of the difference of approach between the computer graphics buff and the engineer, for whom the ambiguities created by such an approach are intolerable. The problem of ensuring coplanarity may be avoided by allowing only triangular faces, which are, of course, always flat. A simpler data structure is made possible when the number of vertices is fixed, but more faces are usually necessary. Figure 5.2 shows the diagrammatic model of Figure 5.1 represented as triangles, while Figures 5.9 and 5.12 show a triangulated model from a real application.

any attempt to calculate, say, the volume of the object is clearly doomed. For these reasons face models are not considered to be reliable *object* representations. Computer graphics users of face models may be very cavalier about such considerations. For instance, suppose that they are writing a program which produces an illusion of transparent surfaces. They may well choose to represent a transparent sheet, say the wall of a wine glass, as a single layer of faces without any actual thickness. The program assumes a notional thickness in computing the image, which looks splendid. Performing engineering analyses on such a construction is impossible.

In most models there will be many vertices on adjacent faces which share the same coordinates. It may therefore be better not to have a simple list of faces, each one independently defined by its vertex coordinates, but to use pointers from each face to a single copy of the coordinates of a vertex, shared between the

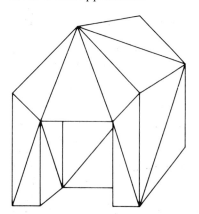

Figure 5.2 The shape of Figure 5.1, modelled with only triangular faces. These faces are simpler, but 33 of them are now required

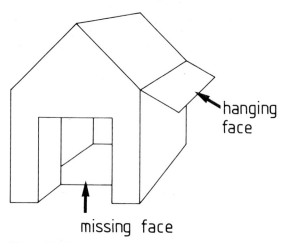

Figure 5.3 Hanging or missing faces are common features of face models used in computer graphics applications

A model created as a number of faces only corresponds to a solid object if the model's creator (person or program) ensures that there is a polygon in the list to correspond to every face of the object. Figure 5.3 shows how it is possible to omit a polygon or to include unconnected or hanging faces. Graphics programs will not baulk at such structures, and the resulting picture may well be quite adequate because, perhaps, the missing face is on the far side of the model from the viewer. However,

faces that use it. Figure 5.4 illustrates this data structure. There is an immediate saving in storage space which is counterbalanced by increased complexity in creating and editing the model. For instance, if a face is being deleted, we cannot automatically delete all its corner vertices, because some of these may also be defining adjacent faces which we may wish to retain. Introducing pointers is, however, a first move towards linking faces together

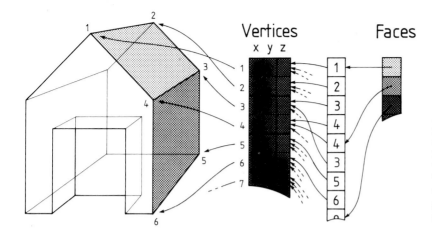

Figure 5.4 The model of Figure 5.1 structured as face records sharing vertex coordinate data. The requirement for vertex coordinate storage is reduced by two-thirds

so that they are guaranteed to be those of a solid object: linked faces are one of the solid model structures that will be discussed in Chapter 7. There are many half-way houses in the amount of linking between faces, edges and vertices. Introducing fewer pointers than are necessary to ensure solidity is simply a matter of algorithmic and storage efficiency, and need not concern us here. We will assume, for the rest of this chapter, that all the faces of a model are stored quite separately. This is the most general approach, as any pointers can easily be eliminated by replacing them by the data to which they point.

Creating face models

Historically, the computer graphics work that produced face models concentrated on processing rather than on input techniques. Constructing a face model by specifying every little face is extremely time-consuming: a machined component with chamfered edges would be a nightmare. As picture generation algorithms improved and could handle a lot of faces it became imperative to have some help from the computer. The simplest techniques involve creating two-dimensional sketches which are then expanded into a set of faces. Most commonly, a face is created corresponding to each line on the sketch, forming a model of which the sketch is the cross-section. Alternatively, faces can be generated to approximate a rotationally symmetric shape. Shapes of revolution have been very popular with the

computer graphics community, particularly tableware such as wine glasses or teapots, on which the latest developments in the simulation of transparency or surface texture can be shown to advantage. These input techniques (Figure 5.5) are similar to the description of two-dimensional shapes using profiles (Figure 3.2). In the present case, however, a three-dimensional representation is explicitly generated, rather than merely implied by the way that data that is actually two-dimensional is employed.

To produce more complicated objects, many of the other shape representations in this book can be converted into face models for display purposes. This is especially common for producing pictures of complex surfaces, where direct use of the surface equations makes sophisticated display techniques very slow. Figure 5.6 shows a duct that has been converted into a face model for hidden-line elimination. Someone with a primary interest in computer graphics can thus view CAE shape representations as input processes for creating face models. On the other hand, an engineer can obtain attractive pictures of his design by converting to a face model, without having to write display programs appropriate to the particular shape representation he is using.

Having been to the trouble of constructing a face model, one easy way to produce a more crowded scene is to make a number of replicas of the original, at different positions in space. We have already met this process in the context of draughting systems, where we

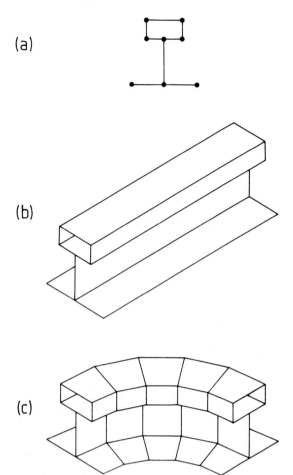

(a)

(b)

(c)

Figure 5.5 A sketch (a) can form the basis for constructing a face model either (b) by converting each line of the sketch into a face perpendicular to the definition plane, or (c) by generating a number of faces to approximate part of a shape of revolution formed by rotating the sketch about a given axis. (Compare with Figure 7.14)

referred to it as instantiation. It has been widely used in preparing scenes to test graphics programs. Half-a-dozen wine glasses look much more impressive than just one, especially if you can see them reflected in each other. Pictures of chess sets have also appeared in the literature, sometimes (for obvious reasons) just a lot of pawns!

This idea of instantiation also has engineering applications. Consider designing a chemical plant, consisting of hundreds of vessels and many miles of pipes, or the service pipework and ducting for a large building. In the chemical industry a scale model is traditionally constructed, at considerable expense, in order to verify that pipes do not foul each other, there is access to the valves, and so forth. Computer programs such as PDMS (Pipework Design and Management System)[48] have been written to replace this physical model, and a great deal of the paperwork surrounding the design of such plant, by a large database and software specifically for plant design. These systems really come into their own when major changes to a design become necessary.

Of course, many of the components in a chemical plant are the same. There may be many, many examples of a single type of valve for instance. Programs like PDMS exploit this fact by storing only one copy of the description of the component, separately from the details of where each one is installed. The simplest use for all this data is to present it in different formats, such as listing valves by supplier, or, say, just listing the ones above a particular size. Analysis functions are also provided, for instance to check that the pipework makes the correct circuits. For the geometrical processes it is necessary to construct a shape model of

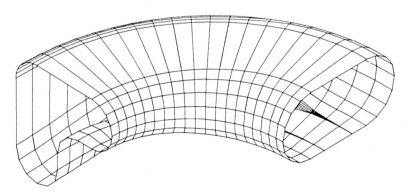

Figure 5.6 The duct of Figure 4.15 is shown here after conversion into a face model and hidden line elimination

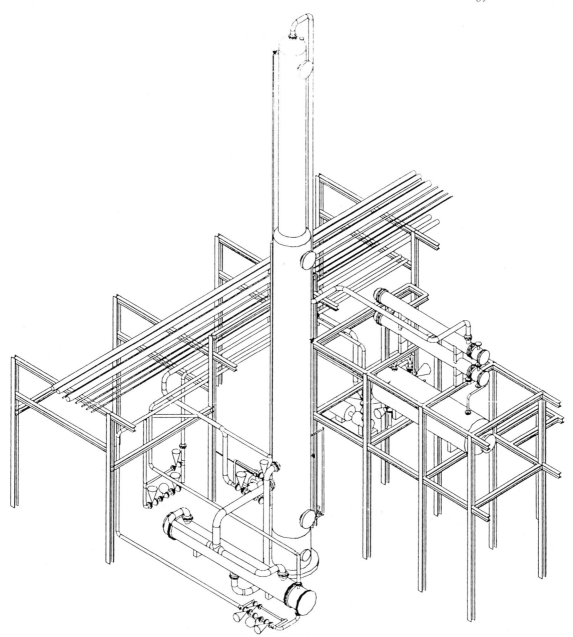

Figure 5.7 Part of a chemical plant represented as a face model. (Isopipe Ltd)

each class of component. Interference calculations can be performed just by using simple shapes, such as cuboids or cylinders, which bound the volume of each component. Some false interferences may be reported but these can be checked by hand: the essential thing is not to miss any. Face models come in when

pictures are needed. The system has a face model of each type of component, and these can be instantiated on a grand scale. Pictures of all or part of the plant may be obtained (Figure 5.7), often from viewpoints that would have been impossible in photographing a physical model. The face models that result from plant layout applications are of course very large and, as we shall see, only some display techniques work quickly on large scenes.

Hidden-line and hidden-surface elimination

Just as more complex surface definitions can be simplified to face models without difficulty, so it is trivial to convert a face model to a wire frame. The wire frame is simply made from the edges of the faces, although it is useful to remove duplicate edges shared by adjacent faces. We can then use all the wire frame display techniques described in Chapter 3. However, the whole point of the face model is to permit more realistic displays, and the first stage in achieving these is to eliminate, in a line drawing, those lines corresponding to edges that would be invisible if the object were solid. We have already said that the face model does not ensure solidity, and it is more realistic to talk of eliminating those edges that are obscured by faces in front of them. *Hidden-line elimination* is the furthest we can go in achieving realism on line drawing devices such as plotters, storage and vector refresh displays. Raster-scan displays allow areas of colour to be achieved by illuminating all the pixels in a given region. With these devices we can potentially produce pictures corresponding much more closely with our real-world view of objects, having characteristics similar to a photograph. In this case it is obviously essential that those faces and parts of faces which are not visible in a particular view of a scene do not appear in it (unless, perhaps, some fancy transparency effect is being used). In general, *hidden-surface elimination* is not optional, like hidden-line elimination, but an integral part of continuous-tone picture production.

A widely respected paper[63] which reviews hidden-line and hidden-surface elimination techniques is about half the length of this book (see also ref. 73, which is much more recent). In the following sections there is only room to outline the approaches that have been taken to the problem. In general, hidden-surface elimination is one of the more time-consuming processes in computer graphics. Because it is essential to the production of realistic scenes a lot of work has been done on fast techniques suitable for real-time animation, especially in ship and flight simulation. In flight simulation especially, the speeds involved require very complex and expensive hardware, and even so the scenes which may be displayed are severely limited in their complexity. We shall not consider hardware dependent approaches, except the relatively simple depth buffer. The efficiency criterion that is of particular importance in CAE is the way in which computation times increase with model size. (In the case of a face model, size may be considered to be the number of faces.) If the rate of increase of computation times is appreciably worse than linear for a given algorithm then that algorithm's applicability is limited to simpler scenes, and the trend in both CAE and computer graphics is towards more complex models and pictures.

Object-space algorithms

Object-space algorithms compute a picture that is as accurate as the original scene. Such a picture can be displayed or plotted at any scale on a device of any resolution (subject only to computer precision). This is most advantageous for line drawings, which often need to be output on a large, accurate, pen plotter. Object-space algorithms are therefore commonly, but not necessarily, associated with hidden-line, rather than hidden-surface, elimination.

Using the 'brute force' approach, every edge of every face is compared, after projection, with all the other faces in turn. Each comparison may leave the edge unchanged, show all of it to be obscured by the face (in this case comparisons stop) or cause it to be split into a number of segments, some visible and some invisible. After all these comparisons, any visible portions of the line remaining are plotted. Because every edge of every face must be compared with every other face, computation times for this approach are proportional to n^2, where n is the number of faces in the scene. This is very unsatisfactory.

One way of speeding things up is to use a *boxing* test. A notional rectangle aligned with the coordinate axes in the plane of projection is

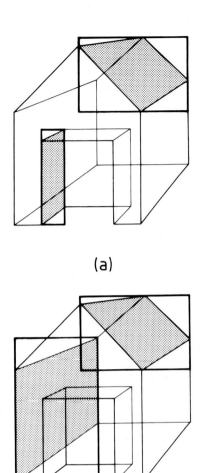

(a)

(b)

Figure 5.8 Boxes drawn around the projections of two faces of a model can be compared prior to comparing the faces themselves. If the boxes do not intersect (a), no further comparison of the faces is necessary. If, on the other hand, the boxes do intersect (b), further computation is needed to determine whether one face does or, as in this case, does not obscure the other.

consideration at an early stage. Unfortunately this only achieves a constant factor of speed increase. The n^2 *order* of the algorithm is unaffected.

A better approach is to divide the area of picture that is being computed into a grid of squares (compare Figure 2.2, where a regular grid is used as a data *structure*). Each square on the grid is associated with a list in which pointers to faces can be recorded. Each face is then compared with the grid and a pointer to the face is added to the list of every square with which it overlaps. The contents of each square can then subsequently be treated in the way mentioned above, as a separate little scene but of vastly lower complexity. By sorting the faces with respect to the grid (sometimes called a *bucket sort* because the data are sorted into fixed compartments or 'buckets'), the computationally devastating process of global comparisons between faces is avoided. The performance of this algorithm depends on a

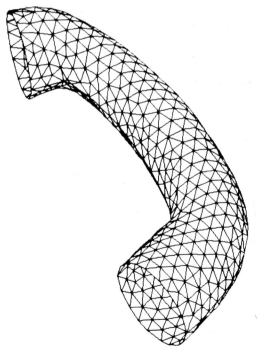

Figure 5.9 A picture of a triangulated face model produced by hidden-line elimination based on dividing the picture plane into a grid. This model is unusual because it was produced from a physical component using a numerically controlled coordinate-measuring machine

constructed for each face. Its limiting coordinates are the maximum and minimum projected coordinate values of the face's vertices, so that the box completely encloses the projection of the face (Figure 5.8). These boxes may be compared with each other more quickly than the individual edges of each face. Many, many pairs of faces that are far away from each other in the image may thus be eliminated from

sensible choice of grid size and is also enhanced when the faces are small and evenly sized. The author has found this a particularly useful algorithm for displaying face models derived from curved surfaces in parallel or isometric projection, where such small and evenly sized faces naturally occur (Figure 5.9).

Image-space algorithms

Image-space algorithms are associated with hidden-surface elimination for pictures on raster-scan displays. It was realized very soon after raster-scan displays became available that the limited and fixed resolution of these devices was a blessing in disguise, in that it could be exploited to simplify and thus to accelerate picture generation. Because a single pixel on a raster scan display can only be one colour at once there is little point in pursuing scene detail that is smaller than pixel size. This allows image-space algorithms to exhibit a performance which is not merely better than proportional to n^2 (recall n is the number of faces) but better than proportional to n. As pictures become more complex an average face corresponds to fewer pixels on the screen. In effect, the faces in a complex scene are displayed at lower resolution than the few, large, faces of a single object.

The simplest way to generate a raster-scan picture is to determine, for every pixel, a line through the scene which corresponds to a notional ray of light passing through the pixel to the viewer's eye. We then compare this with all the faces in the scene, calculate which faces are cut by this ray, and which of these intersections is nearest the viewer. The colour of the face corresponding to this nearest intersection is then written into that pixel. *Ray-casting*, as this process is called, may be viewed as the reverse of projection (Figure 3.20): we proceed from a point on the screen to a point on the model, instead of from the model to the screen. Ray-casting is conveniently linear in computation time with scene complexity, but the absolute times are very large because of the number of pixels on a typical display screen. It is therefore normally only used with face models when complex lighting effects are to be produced.

To improve on the performance of this basic approach we can exploit the *coherence* of the picture we are trying to generate. One example of this is *scan-line coherence*. In most pictures, many of the faces which appear in a given horizontal line of pixels (called a scan-line, because this is the raster order in which the electron beam scans the display) will appear in the next: the picture does not change all that quickly down the screen (Figure 5.10). To make use of this, algorithms create a list of the faces that intersect with the topmost scan-line of the picture, and the edges at which colour transitions take place along the line. As picture

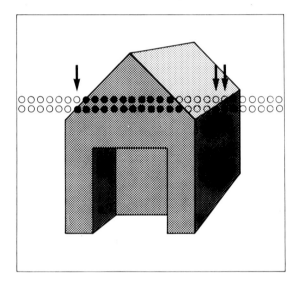

Figure 5.10 Hidden line algorithms can exploit scan-line coherence because relatively few pixels (shown here as circles) change colour from one scan-line to the next (in this case, the ones arrowed)

generation proceeds down the screen this information is updated. Consideration of all faces is thus restricted to once in each scan-line rather than once for every point. These algorithms are particularly useful for real-time picture generation because the picture emerges in raster order.

Warnock's algorithm[70] has had a wide influence on all kinds of computer graphics work, as well as the hidden-surface problem. It exploits not the scan-line coherence but the *area coherence* of a picture: the fact that adjacent small areas are very often the same colour. Initially, Warnock's algorithm considers the entire picture, which for simplicity we will assume to be square. If there are no faces which appear in the picture it is blank. If a single face covers it entirely it can be drawn as one big square of a single colour. Normally this will not be possible (or we will have to look at a lot of very boring pictures) and the algorithm then tries to simplify the problem presented to it by dividing the picture area into four new squares each half the size (a quarter the area) of the whole. Each of these is then treated exactly as though it were the original screen: if there are no faces that appear within the square it is left blank or, if a single face covers it, a square of colour is drawn. Otherwise it is divided again and so on. This is a recursive process (like the B-spline equation in the last chapter): the algorithm is invoking itself to work on the smaller pieces of picture. Of course, division cannot continue indefinitely and, at some places on the picture (such as the joints between adjacent faces), however many times we divide we will not be able to meet cither the criterion to leave a blank or that to plot a square of a single colour. However, since a single pixel on the screen can only be one colour, when division has proceeded down to pixel level we simply make a choice between

the colours of all the faces that are still being considered. One logical way to do this is to cast a ray corresponding to the centre of the pixel. The effect of applying Warnock's algorithm is that division down to pixel size occurs only at the edges of the frontmost faces of the scene. Figure 5.11 shows the pattern that the division takes. Note that, like the grid used in bucket sorting, we have already met the Warnock division used as a method of structuring data (Figure 2.3).

Explanation of either sort of coherence means that computation times are essentially determined by the length of the edges visible in the picture. This is an important factor if we are considering computing the same picture at different screen resolutions. As screen resolution increases, the number of pixels involved in edges increases linearly with it, while the total number of pixels on the screen is proportional to the square of the resolution. Scan-line and Warnock algorithms are therefore more attractive than ray-casting at higher screen resolutions.

Depth sorting algorithms

The *depth-priority*, or 'painter's' hidden-surface algorithm sorts the faces in a scene into order of distance from the viewer and then sends them in this order to the display, where later arrivals overwrite earlier ones. The front faces, which arrive last, are those which correctly form the final picture. This is not quite as easy as it sounds, because a unique ordering of the faces is not necessarily possible: three faces may be mutually overlapping, in the fashion of an iris diaphragm. These cases are resolved by splitting one face in the plane of another. The sorting process necessary with this algorithm can be shown to limit its performance with complexity to $n \log n$, but it is convenient for simple scenes such as that of Figure 5.12.

Linear performance can be achieved, however, by using a special piece of hardware, the *depth buffer*. This is like a raster-scan device, but with sufficient storage for two numbers corresponding to each pixel in the picture. One is its colour, the other an expression of its distance from the viewer. Operation is simplicity itself. Each face is

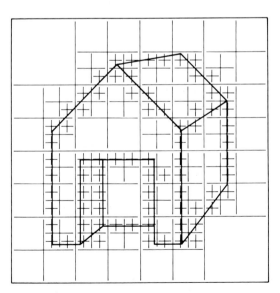

Figure 5.11 The pattern of divisions produced by Warnock's algorithm. This figure is diagrammatic: in practice division is down to pixel level

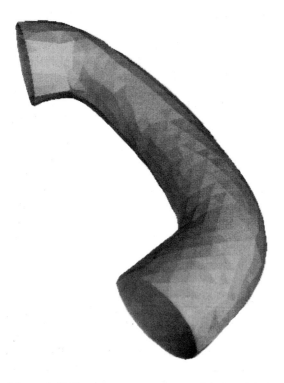

Figure 5.12 Continuous tone picture of the model of Figure 5.9, produced using the painter's algorithm. (The illumination was computed with a Lambert's law lighting model)

considered in turn, and converted after projection into pixels corresponding to the area it covers, with a depth associated with each pixel. These depths are fed into the depth buffer and compared with the depths already recorded at each pixel. If the new depth is further from the viewer the new face cannot be seen and the new information is discarded. If the new depth is nearer it replaces the old entry and the colour of the new face is also written into that pixel. The time this device takes to produce a picture will clearly be proportional to the sum of the areas of all the faces in the scene. Graphics devices have been constructed on this principle to generate colour pictures directly from face information supplied by a remote computer. These displays are quite fast and can save programming effort, but there can be occasional wrongly-coloured pixels in the resulting pictures, especially where faces meet, due to limited resolution of the depth data.

Figure 5.18 was in fact produced on such a device.

Realistic pictures

In this section we shall look briefly at a number of techniques for enhancing the correspondence between the pictures we produce and scenes in the real world. At the current state of development the computational effort required for many of these processes is usually felt to be excessive for CAE applications. Exceptions to this include components which determine the appearance of a consumer product.

Lighting models

When computing a continuous-tone picture from a face model it is possible to assign a colour to each face manually. In general, it is more useful to allow a program to calculate a number of different shades depending on the relationship between the object and some specified lighting, having merely indicated to the program the basic colour of the object: the colour it was painted, so to speak. The computation of these resulting shades is performed using a *lighting model*. This may be quite simple, or try to correspond quite closely to the physics of actual lighting. In the latter case there will inevitably be a lot of computing to be done.

The simplest lighting models are based on Lambert's law. This states that the intensity i_R of reflected light leaving a surface in any direction is equal to the intensity of the incident light i_I multiplied by the cosine of the angle θ between the normal to that surface and the direction of incidence of the light (Figure 5.13):

$$i_R = i_I \cos \theta$$

Surfaces facing away from the light appear black if this formula is used exactly. A simple way to allow for the diffuse lighting usually present in reality is to add a constant term i_D:

$$i_R = i_D + i_I \cos \theta$$

This formula is adequate to allow pictures of face models, after hidden-surface elimination, to be perceived as 'realistic'. If we assume that

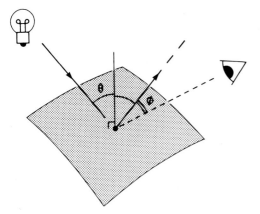

Figure 5.13 The intensity of Lambert's law lighting is based on the angle θ between the incident light and the surface normal. Specular reflection is computed from the angle φ between a reflected light ray and the viewing direction

the source of light is sufficiently distant from the objects being illuminated for the arriving rays to be considered as parallel (Figure 5.14), then any flat surface will appear in a uniform shade. We may therefore compute the colours of all the faces of a model before projection or hidden-surface elimination. As pieces of the picture are generated they may be displayed without further ado. The introduction of any more sophisticated lighting causes an abrupt increase in computation costs, as every pixel in the picture must be considered individually to determine its shade. Like ray-casting, this is very time-consuming.

As a first step towards more complex lighting, we may specify a point source of light. The angle of the incident light now varies from point to point over a surface and, moreover, the intensity of the arriving light varies as the inverse of the square of the distance s from the source. The reflected intensity is calculated as

$$i_R = i_D + \frac{i_I \cos \theta}{s^2}$$

using Lambert's law again. Figure 5.16 shows a scene illuminated with a single point light source. Multiple light sources may be accommodated by considering each source in turn and summing their contributions—at an appropriate increase in computation cost, of course.

Our lighting model may be further enhanced

by making some allowances for *specular reflection*. On a shiny surface, light which leaves the surface with an angle near the angle of incidence tends to have the colour of the source of the light rather than of the object. The object is acting as a mirror and this produces 'highlights' on the image. This effect is especially noticeable on curved surfaces: try holding an apple up to the light. Figure 6.13 shows the effect of specular reflection in displaying a surface patch. In this case the intensity of the specular reflection was calculated as $\cos^n \phi$, where φ is the angle between the reflected light ray and the viewing direction (Figure 5.13). This is purely a convenient numerical device: the exact physical process is much more complex. The higher the value of n, the 'shinier' the surface appears.

Shadows

The computing of shadows is expensive to perform and often counter-productive in CAE applications. Product inspectors and others spend a lot of time shining little lights into nooks and crannies of components to examine detail that is otherwise obscured in shadow. Shadowless computer-generated images, although 'unrealistic', allow detail over the whole of the visible surface of the model to be perceived with a clarity unmatched by reality itself.

If there is a requirement for shadowing, then the problem that has to be solved is in many ways similar to hidden-surface elimination. With a single light source the regions in shadow are those that cannot be 'seen' from that light source position. We may implement a shadowing algorithm in exactly this way. The first application of a hidden-surface technique defines areas on the individual faces which are, and those which are not, in shadow. The second hidden-surface elimination process generates the parts of this shadowed scene which are visible to the viewer, as usual. Alternatively, if we are using ray-casting, then, having traced each ray from the viewpoint onto the object, we can create and trace a second ray back to the light source. If this strikes another part of the object then the original point is in shadow, otherwise not. This technique was used in the generation of Figures 5.15, 5.16 and 5.17.

Figure 5.14 A picture of a model of a vertical milling machine and its controller produced using parallel illumination and a Lambert's law lighting model. (This figure and Figures 5.15, 5.16 and 5.17 were actually computed from a faceted solid model, not a face model)

Figure 5.15 The view of Figure 5.14, but with shadows computed by ray-casting

Figure 5.16 The view of Figure 5.14, but with a point light source and shadows, both computed by ray-casting

Figure 5.17 The view of Figure 5.14, but with parallel illumination and an additional point light source in front of the spindle of the milling machine. Shadows have been calculated for the point source lighting only. The picture was generated by ray-casting

Shading

In trying to produce representations of curved objects, computer graphics people have been reluctant to abandon flat-faced models, for which a wide range of proven display techniques now exist. Instead they have developed ways of colouring the pictures of objects actually composed of large flat faces in a way that gives the illusion of smoothly curving shapes. The process is confusingly called *shading*. Pictures which deliberately fool the viewer undermine the rationale for pursuing graphics within CAE, which is to communicate shape information as accurately as possible. However, shading is not entirely useless to the engineer. Figure 5.18 shows ducts which have been converted to a face model and then shaded. Because the faces are small, the final picture may be expected to be very similar to the one that we would obtain by precise

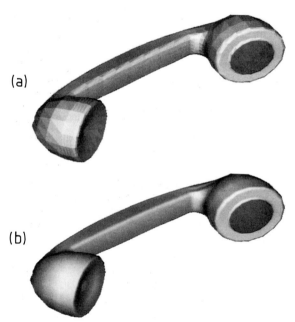

(a)

(b)

Figure 5.18 The model of Figure 4.20, composed of three ducts blended together, is displayed here after conversion to a face model. Hidden-surface elimination has been achieved using a depth buffer. A Lambert's law lighting model (a) was used; this was then supplemented (b) by Gouraud shading. Note that the polygonal horizon of the face model is still visible in the Gouraud-shaded picture. (Delta Computer Aided Engineering Ltd)

computations on the original duct definition. By taking this rather devious route it was possible to make use of a special graphics device which could perform the display calculations much faster than a general purpose computer. Furthermore, this route to pictures remains available, without any reprogramming, even if we make changes to the algebra we use to describe surfaces.

The shading process is essentially one of interpolation. It was pioneered by Gouraud.[35] Using his algorithm, a vector is calculated at every vertex where adjacent flat faces meet, which is the average of the vectors normal to the meeting faces. (Note that this implies more structure in the model than the simplest case where all the faces are quite independent.) From this averaged surface normal an intensity is calculated using the lighting model. The intensity at any point on a face is then obtained by linear interpolation from the corner values. This technique, which was used to produce the picture in Figure 5.18(b), is computationally quite efficient, but intensity discontinuities may still be observable at face boundaries. A perceptual effect, known as Mach banding, tends unfortunately to enhance the noticeability of any such discontinuity by making the lighter side of the boundary appear lighter still and the dark side darker. Phong shading[54] is a more sophisticated but more time-consuming technique. It involves interpolating the normal vector itself and applying the lighting model separately to each of the notional surface normals thus generated. This reduces Mach banding and is also more satisfactory in rendering specular reflection.

Colour

In the preceding section we have indicated how lighting considerations may be taken into account geometrically. It is also necessary to compute the actual colours to display. In the case of monochrome images this is relatively straightforward. Characteristics of both light sources and illuminated surfaces may be stated in terms of intensity alone. However, we should make allowance both for non-linearities in the display system and also for the human perception of intensity as a logarithmic function. This latter effect means that, to perceive a smooth progression, more closely spaced values should be supplied at low than at high intensities.

When chromatic colour itself is introduced the situation becomes much more complicated. Television tubes work by illuminating phosphor dots of the so-called three primary colours: red, green and blue. There are three types of colour receptor on the retina, each responsive to red, green or blue light, so a television tube can produce, as we know from experience, an effect corresponding to most of the colours we perceive in real life, even though the actual spectrum emitted by the real object may be very different from that emitted from the picture on the screen. Colours can be created by defining specified proportions of red, green and blue directly, but it is often more satisfactory to use the concepts of hue, saturation and intensity. Because equal amounts of red, green and blue light are perceived as white, we may consider any colour as a proportion of white light, with additional amounts of two of the primaries only. The choice and amounts of these additional primaries relative to each other is said to determine the *hue* of the colour, while

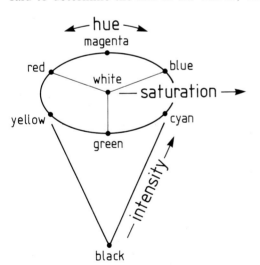

Figure 5.19 A colour cone showing the relationship between hue, saturation and intensity. A colour is represented by a point within the volume of the cone

the sum of their contributions, relative to the amount of white, determines the *saturation*. The *intensity* of the colour is the total amount of light of all colours. The colour cone of Figure 5.19 should help to explain these quantities. Moving towards the centre reduces its saturation until white is eventually reached. At this point hue is meaningless. Intensity is the third dimension and varies along the axis of the cone. At the apex there is zero intensity and hence both hue and saturation are undefined.

In using colour there are a number of problems in achieving realism. We must choose realistic colours, or at least colours which satisfy the user. We must determine the way that colours interact in the scene: coloured objects will interact with coloured light to determine the colour of light that is reflected. Lastly we must make corrections for device and perceptive non-linearities which are much more complex than in the monochromatic case. These matters are beyond the scope of this book but are well dealt with by Foley and Van Dam.[27]

The engineering user is usually able to tolerate a greater departure from realism in the matter of colour than in any other respect. Often it will be more important simply to have different parts of a model coloured in a way that allows them to be differentiated, without any attempt to obtain, say, the reflective properties of a real metallic surface. A perfectly readable picture results if proportions of red, green and blue are chosen as the basic colour of each object in the scene and surfaces at angles to the light are coloured with a reduced intensity calculated from Lambert's law. The hue, intensity and saturation model perhaps makes it easier to choose colours, but no further refinements are necessary to produce a workable, if inexact, system. The picture on the front cover is a good example of a diagrammatic colour scheme that actually provides more information than a realistic view. In this case each hole in the component is coloured to indicate the method used to machine it.

6

Sculptured surfaces

In Chapter 4 we examined surfaces of which the cross-sections are the features of primary interest. The cross-sections of a duct can be closely controlled, but the shape that results along the duct is essentially a secondary result of the way the surface is defined. In this chapter we shall look at representing objects where our main concern is the overall aesthetic impression produced by the shape. These *sculptured surface* techniques are intended to permit a designer to work directly in terms of the skin of the object, and to control its more subtle properties, the 'accents' of shape, directly. The classic application of sculptured surface techniques is in designing road vehicle bodies. There are also many smaller consumer goods, such as power tools and kitchen appliances, which also often have a rounded, indeed sometimes rather comically 'stream-lined', appearance. There are of course reasons other than appearance for using sculptured surfaces, and these were discussed at the beginning of Chapter 4.

Patches

If we have a large surface to construct it is unlikely that we shall find a single equation to describe it all. Even if we could, it would probably be an algebraic nightmare. This problem has already occurred with long curves, which we found it better to design piecewise as splines. In a similar way we can construct a large surface from a number of pieces. These *patches* must be formulated in a controllable way which also facilitates joining them together without discontinuities (Figure 6.1).

By far the most common type of sculptured surface element is the *bi-parametric patch*,[28] of which the following sections contain examples. This has one equation for each of x, y, and z, like a space curve, but each equation is in

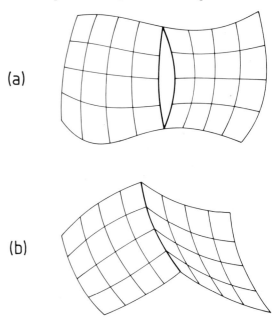

(a)

(b)

Figure 6.1 Faults in joints between sculptured surface patches include (a) gaps and (b) slope discontinuities

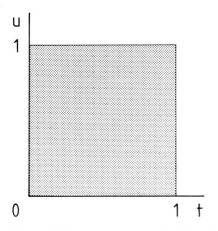

Figure 6.2 Patches are normally defined over a unit square in parameter

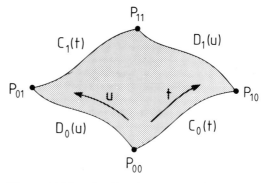

Figure 6.3 Notation for edge curves and corner points used in the Coons patch definition (explained in the text)

terms of not one but two parameters, which we will refer to as t and u. A patch, like a curve, is defined over a certain range of parameter values. This is commonly $0 \leqslant t \leqslant 1$ and $0 \leqslant u \leqslant 1$. These limits define a square region in 'parameter space': u plotted against t (Figure 6.2). Patches defined in this way are said to be 'parametrically square'. Of course, they do not correspond to exact squares in (x, y, z) space, but they usually work best providing a near-rectangular piece of surface. The reader might like to think of a rectangular piece of sheet rubber, which can be stretched and bent into different shapes, but still retains a certain 'squareness'.

Coons patches

The *Coons patch*[17] is a method of blending together four space curves bounding the region to be patched. One of its main advantages is that these curves need only be parametric: no particular form of equation is necessary. Suppose that a patch is to be created bounded by the curves $\mathbf{C}_0(t)$, $\mathbf{C}_1(t)$, $\mathbf{D}_0(u)$ and $\mathbf{D}_1(u)$, as shown in Figure 6.3. The vector notation being employed uses, for example, $\mathbf{C}_0(t)$ to represent three parametric equations in t, one each for x, y and z. Now we are going to construct two blending functions, which we will call f and g. They are used in conjunction with both parameters in turn and will appear as, say, $f(t)$ or $f(u)$ as appropriate. Their function is to vary the contribution of each curve to the patch as

the parameter values change. There is some flexibility possible in the choice of the blending functions, but they must fulfil the following conditions:

$$f(0) = 1, f(1) = 0$$
$$g(0) = 0, g(1) = 1$$
$$f(s) = g(1 - s)$$

(The variable s is standing in for either t or u.) The simplest acceptable blending functions (Figure 6.4) are linear ones:

$$f(s) = 1 - s$$
$$g(s) = s$$

The reader might be tempted to guess that the sort of patch surface we require would result from the equation

$$\mathbf{Q}(t,u) = \mathbf{C}_0(t)f(u) + \mathbf{C}_1(t)g(u) + \mathbf{D}_0(u)f(t) + \mathbf{D}_1(u)g(t)$$

where the weight applied to each curve is 1 at its own end of the patch, and 0 at the other end. However, if we consider a corner of the patch it can be seen that both the curves meeting there contribute to that point, giving just double the correct value of each coordinate. It is therefore necessary to modify the above equation by subtracting a blended combination of the corner point coordinates, in a way that restores the correct coordinate values at the patch boundaries. We shall refer to the corner point coordinates as $\mathbf{P}_{00}$, $\mathbf{P}_{01}$, $\mathbf{P}_{10}$ and $\mathbf{P}_{11}$, as shown in Figure 6.3, where each such symbol, like the others defined so far, is a

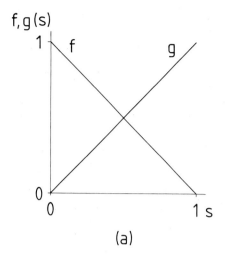

(a)

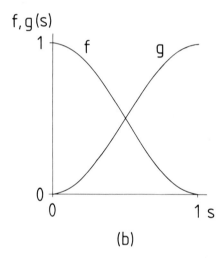

(b)

Figure 6.4 (a) Linear and (b) cubic blending functions used in the formulation of Coons patches

vector quantity referring to all three coordinates. This gives the actual Coons patch equation:

$$
\begin{aligned}
Q(t,u) = \ &C_0(t)f(u) + C_1(t)g(u) \\
&+ D_0(u)f(t) + D_1(u)g(t) \\
&- P_{00}f(t)f(u) - P_{01}f(t)g(u) \\
&- P_{10}g(t)f(u) - P_{11}g(t)g(u)
\end{aligned}
$$

The resulting patch will span the four boundaries provided. A point on it can be generated by supplying values of t and u to each of the three equations, one for each coordinate direction, and thus generating the values of x, y and z.

Two patches which share a common edge curve will obviously be continuous but, in most places on a sculptured surfaced component, we will also require a smooth joint between adjacent patches, represented by continuity of the surface normal. In order for this to be achieved we must make more demands on the blending functions. They must have zero slope, that is be horizontal, at their ends. A smooth joint between adjacent patches can then be achieved, provided that the edges of adjacent

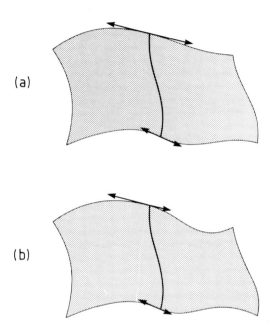

(a)

(b)

Figure 6.5 In order to achieve a smooth joint between Coons patches that share an edge the differentials of the boundary curves at the shared corners must either be (a) equal or (b) in constant ratio. In addition, the same blending functions must be used in the generation of each patch

patches that meet at the shared edge fulfil the appropriate continuity conditions shown in Figure 6.5. The simplest blending functions (Figure 6.4) that meet these new requirements are cubics, such as:

$$
\begin{aligned}
f(s) &= 1 - 3s^2 + 2s^3 \\
g(s) &= 3s^2 - 2s^3
\end{aligned}
$$

Figure 6.6 shows a Coons patch constructed using these blending functions, and forming part of the surface of a simple component.

Coons patch blending functions to achieve this goal are also cubics.

If all the boundaries of a Coons patch, and the blending functions, are cubics, then, looking back at the Coons patch equation, we see that the resulting surface equation will consist entirely of polynomials in t and u, with no term of higher order than t^3u^3. Each of the equations for x, y and z will have 16 terms. If we specify the four edge curves and the two blending functions the coefficients of all these terms will be determined as part of the Coons formulation. Alternatively, we may abandon our boundary curves and blending functions and find all 16 coefficients by substituting particular values of position or derivative that we require at particular parametric points on the surface into the patch equations (Figure

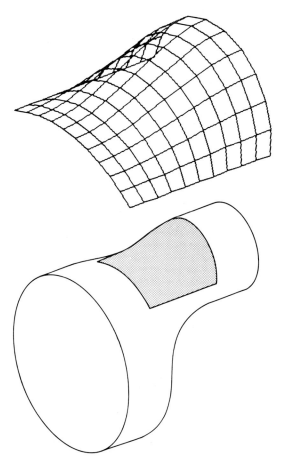

Figure 6.6 An example Coons patch with two different circular arcs and two straight line segments as its edges. It is displayed (top) as a grid of isoparametric lines. A possible application for the patch (above) is in a joint between two offset cylinders of different diameters. In this case patching is an alternative to a cross-sectional surface

Cartesian product patches

One of the great merits of the Coons patch is that it does not commit us to a particular form of boundary curve. In practice, the most commonly used patch edge is the parametric cubic. As we saw in Chapter 4, this has sufficient flexibility to meet both position and slope constraints at its ends. It is thus the simplest curve which permits us to specify patch corner conditions with sufficient flexibility to ensure a controlled first derivative and hence smooth joints. Note that the simplest

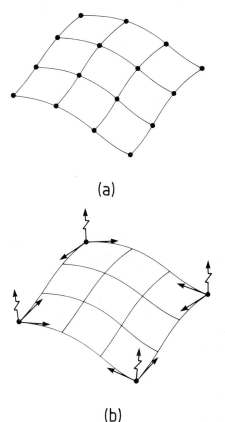

(a)

(b)

Figure 6.7 Cartesian product surfaces can be specified by (a) Lagrangian interpolation between a grid of points, or (b) by Hermite interpolation between corner points, corner slopes in both parametric directions, and twist vectors

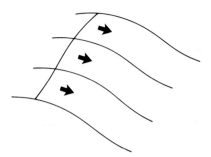

Figure 6.8 A Cartesian product patch can be visualized as a parametric cubic sliding along a set of parametric cubics parametrically orthogonal to it

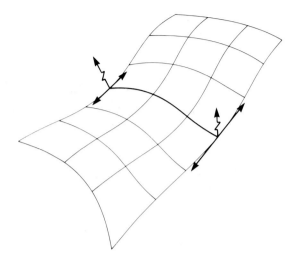

Figure 6.9 A smooth joint between Cartesian product patches can be achieved if they share an edge and differentials and twist vectors are matched at the shared corners. (Alternatively, it is possible to formulate a constant ratio condition, analogous to that for the Coons patch)

6.7). This is an exact analogy with the processes of Lagrangian and Hermite interpolation that we used to decide on the coefficients of parametric curves in Chapter 4. A surface defined in this way is called a *Cartesian product patch*,[25] because the terms are the products of the terms of two curve equations. For any constant value of either parameter the equation reduces to a polynomial in the other. A bicubic Cartesian product surface may therefore be thought of as one cubic 'sliding' along a set of cubics in the other parametric direction (Figure 6.8).

Cartesian product patches may be constructed by a process of Lagrangian interpolation between 16 data points, often arranged as a four-by-four grid. This does not assist us in making a big patched surface because smooth joints between patches cannot be guaranteed. It is therefore more usual to define Cartesian product patches by the positions and partial derivatives at their corner points. However, the four positional constraints and eight slope constraints ($\partial Q/\partial t$ and $\partial Q/\partial u$ at each corner) only provide 12 pieces of data, and 16 are needed to allow the 16 coefficients of the patch to be determined. The final four are usually supplied by so-called 'twist vectors', or cross-parameter gradients $\partial^2 Q/\partial t\partial u$ at each corner, sketched in Figure 6.7. By matching gradients and twist vectors at the shared corners of adjacent patches, slope continuity across the joint can be assured (Figure 6.9).

In practice, the problem of choosing values for these twist vectors has discouraged users of the bicubic Cartesian product patch, although it has appeared in a number of practical implementations such as the POLYSURF[26] and NMG (Numerical Master Geometry)[61] systems. The choice of suitable values for both derivatives and twist vectors is hampered by dimensional problems. Sensible values for the derivatives and twists may be orders of magnitude different from the positional information. In a form proposed by Ferguson,[25] this problem is partially overcome by the simple expedient of setting the twist vector magnitudes to zero. Unfortunately, this leads to perceptible flattening at the corners between patches. Although Ferguson patches have been incorporated into the APT (Automatically Programmed Tool)[59] numerical control language, users of this system have tended to end up needing more, smaller, patches than with, say, NMG, in which the twist vectors are determined from a piecewise interpolation across the whole surface, similar to a spline.

Bézier and B-spline patches

Just as the Bézier formulation was able to overcome some of the difficulties in specifying parametric curves, it also comes to the rescue of the parametric patch. The Bézier patch[6,29] has the equation:

$$\mathbf{Q}(t,u) = \sum_{i=0}^{i=m} \sum_{j=0}^{j=n} \frac{m!}{(m-i)!i!} \frac{n!}{(n-j)!j!}$$
$$\times t^i(1-t)^{m-i}u^j(1-u)^{n-j}\mathbf{P}_{i,j}$$

Although it looks rather complicated, the relationship with the Bézier curve equation should readily be apparent. In the Bézier patch the control points $P_{i,j}$ are arranged as a grid over the surface. For a bicubic Bézier patch, for instance, a four-by-four grid of points is needed (Figure 6.10). The outermost 12 grid points control the boundary curves. The four points on the inside of the grid 'pull' the patch towards them in the way that we should now be

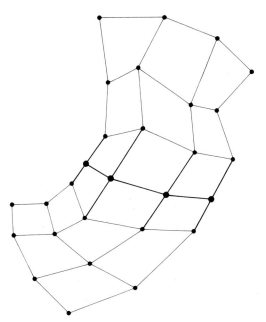

expecting. Effectively, these interior grid points provide the four pieces of information that were otherwise supplied by the notorious twist vectors. Of course, in the end, the Bézier formulation produces an equation algebraically identical to the Cartesian product. Only the method of interpolation is different. Bézier patches can be joined together with both positional and slope continuity by enforcing conditions on the two rows of points in the mesh which correspond to the side of the patch where the joint is to be made (Figure 6.11). Unfortunately, as more patches are added into a surface the proportion of mesh points that are not predetermined rapidly declines. The only way to obtain more flexibility is to use higher-order patches. With Bézier patches the number of grid points rises as the square of the

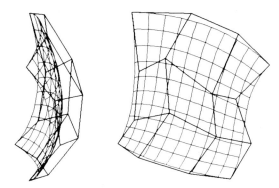

Figure 6.10 A bicubic Bézier patch created from a 4 × 4 grid of points and displayed here as two orthographic views

Figure 6.11 Joints between Bézier patches can be achieved by ensuring that the control grids share a row of points, and also that the points on this row and the next row in on each patch are collinear in sets of three. Further, the distance between each point on the shared row and the corresponding points on the next row on each patch must be in a constant ratio. (The upper patch is that of Figure 6.10)

order of the edge polynomials. The grids can soon become very cumbersome, although only the points away from the edge of each grid are free for the user to specify.

Large patches can be created, without requiring high-order equations, by using B-splines[33] rather than Bézier curves as a basis. The B-spline patch definition is:

$$\mathbf{Q}(t,u) = \sum_{i=0}^{i=m} \sum_{j=0}^{j=n} \mathbf{B}_{i,k}(t)\mathbf{B}_{j,k}(u)\mathbf{P}_{i,j}$$

This equation uses the polynomials that were defined in Chapter 4, and here we assume that the order of the patch (k) is the same in each direction, which usually makes things easier. Note, however, that the grid can be made rectangular rather than square by choosing different values for m and n, which is a useful improvement on the Bézier form. Large patches also make more sense using B-splines because the localization of the track points' control that we saw with B-spline curves applies to the grid points' control of the patch. The influence of a single mesh vertex extends over a defined parametrically square region of the patch surface. Therefore large B-spline patches can provide the same degree of control as a number of Bézier patches, while avoiding the need for so many joints.

Creating patched surfaces

Patched surfaces may be created by a process of surface fitting to a digitized physical model. This is a more sophisticated version of interpolation which looks for a best rather than an exact surface through measured data. It is common practice in the motor car industry, where body stylists produce a full-size clay model at an early stage in realizing a new design. Surface fitting is not without its difficulties. There can, for example, be problems in choosing a strategy to divide the surface between different patches and then sorting out waviness or unwanted 'accents' introduced by the fitting process.

If there is no physical model the user has the choice of two strategies in creating a surface. The first is to decide on a single patch, commonly the most important part of the object, and then to move outwards from that first patch, supplying control parameters to 'mop up' surplus degrees of freedom in succeeding patches. The second strategy is to define a mesh of patch edges and then to fill in the patches between them. The mesh must consist of lines in essentially two directions, and these must obviously meet at crossing points. We have the further option of creating the mesh itself on an incremental basis, but it may be easier to avoid a wavy surface if each mesh line is a continuous spline curve, meeting the curves in the other direction at their mutual knots.

Display techniques

In practice, the initial definition of the surface, whether from scratch or from a physical model, is likely to represent only a small part of the total amount of work involved in creating the shape. Subsequently there will be a long iterative process of making changes and

assessing them. Components with geometrically simple surfaces can often be verified, except for details of dimension, by a glance at one or two views. This is not the case with patched surfaces, because of their subtlety and because the designer's requirements may themselves be nebulous. Sculptured surfaced components are often fundamental to the appearance of a product and can be the subject of a lengthy appraisal by many people. Because of these considerations the interactive design of sculptured surfaces cannot be divorced from the visualization techniques available.[31]

The control of the various patches we have just described may be effected by a choice of numerical values. More often, the user creates and modifies geometric control structures, such as points on a Bézier grid, or slope vectors. These can only be used sensibly in the context of the three-dimensional information that is already present. Special, but rather cumbersome, graphics hardware is available which can give a limited illusion of three-dimensional space. On an ordinary display the only sensible procedure is to enter the control data using two or more simultaneous views of the object, as already seen in Figure 6.10. Two coordinates of a control point may be specified in one of the views and the missing coordinate added in a second. In any case, control structures such as Bézier grids are vastly more difficult to specify reliably than their two-dimensional equivalents.

However many views are made available to the user, some form of rendering of the surfaces under construction must be provided in each of them. The most common way of displaying patched surfaces is to plot a mesh of curves of constant parameter, because these are very easy to generate by choosing a value for one parameter in the patch equation and then incrementing the other. Many people are accustomed to seeing curves of constant parameter, but they can be misleading. In particular, two identical patches can be parameterized in different ways (Figure 6.12) and it is doubtful if they are then perceived as the same surface. If we are using curves of constant parameter these can be displayed as three-dimensional straight line segments, which effectively comprise a wire frame. The legibility of this sort of picture may be enhanced with

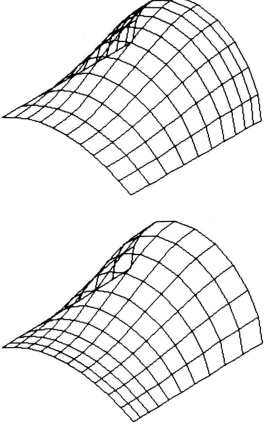

Figure 6.12 Isoparametric curves plotted for two different parameterizations of the same patch (the Coons patch of Figure 6.6)

any of the techniques mentioned in Chapter 2. Haloing is especially effective, because with a fine mesh very little remains of the line segments behind the frontmost surface. Some suppression of hidden detail is essential if there are many patches making up a convoluted surface.

Lines of constant parameter can be made the basis for yet further types of picture by converting the parametrically square regions between the lines into small faces, as we did with cross-sectional surfaces, and displaying the resulting face model with any of the techniques of Chapter 5. Conversion into a face model is a computationally efficient way to perform hidden-line elimination, but the greater realism of a shaded display may be required. In that case we can employ the

approximate shading techniques from the last chapter (Figure 5.18) or use the original patch equations directly (Figure 6.13). A sensible combination of relatively fast operations on the approximate faces and slow but accurate computations on the exact surfaces can produce a good compromise between speed and a faithful rendering.

There are a couple of other display techniques that are sometimes used for patched

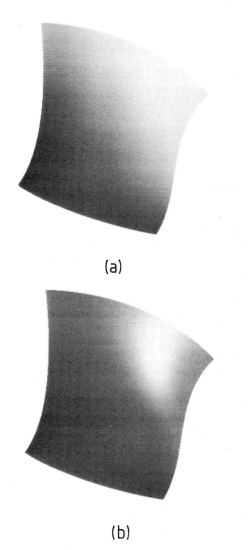

(a)

(b)

Figure 6.13 The bicubic patch of Figure 6.10 displayed (a) with Lambert's law lighting and (b) with Lambert's law lighting and a model of specular reflection

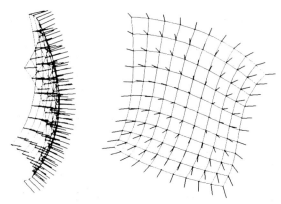

Figure 6.14 The bicubic patch of Figure 6.10 displayed with a line segment, corresponding to the surface normal, plotted at each intersection of the isoparametric lines (sometimes called a 'hedgehog plot'). The normals are of constant length

surfaces, as ways of presenting extra information about the surface rather than enhancing realism. One of these (Figure 6.14) is to display normals to the surface as lines sticking out at convenient intervals, often at the junctions of isoparametric lines. By visually comparing the angles of these, the user may be able to detect waviness in the surface that would not otherwise be apparent. Because, as we shall see, the offsetting process which is required to machine these surfaces requires the generation of

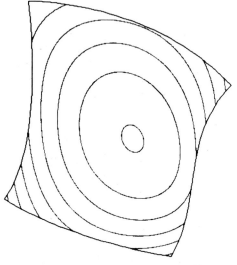

Figure 6.15 The bicubic patch of Figure 6.10 displayed as intersections with a set of parallel planes perpendicular to the viewing direction

normals, displaying them can give some help in the choice of a cutter and a cutting direction. Another technique sometimes employed is to generate the intersections of the object with a series of parallel planes. The planes may be perpendicular to the viewing direction, giving a display like a contour map (Figure 6.15), or the sectioning and viewing directions may be different. Because the section planes have a known separation, this technique, like a contour map, presents the surface data in a way that allows numerical statements to be made about features: for instance, the actual depth of a hollow. Some objects, like motor car bodies, will have natural sectioning directions. In other cases, when a direction is not obvious, very different pictures are presented as viewing and sectioning directions are changed. It is sometimes helpful to use this technique to exaggerate any suspected unevenness in a part of a shape by sectioning in a direction approximately tangential to the surface at the region of interest.

Finally, the complexity of the surface we are attempting to design may defeat the most subtle graphical display technique. In this case there is no alternative but to manufacture a prototype for assessment. So frequently is this necessary that special model-making machines, with high speed cutters designed to machine models very rapidly from structural foam, have been designed. Alternatively, conventional NC machine tools may be used at high feed rates to cut test-pieces from blocks of wax. These processes are not necessarily wildly slower than computing, say, a shaded picture with a very accurate lighting model. The foam or wax model can give information about the feel of a surface that is clearly not available from the display, and tiny surface irregularities, which may have been only suspicions on the display, can be investigated, provided of course that the cutter path is sufficiently fine. If, on the other hand, the overall effect is the major concern, a high resolution shaded display may well be much more informative than a matt, putty-coloured piece of foam or wax.

Intersections and blends

We have already alluded to the difficulty of breaking up a surface into patches. This is a process that must be performed at the earliest stage, before any of the surface is in place, although some revision may be possible. It can thus only be done correctly by someone with experience of the system in use. He has to decide the orientation of the patch boundaries, and also how large the patches are going to be in a given area. If a few large patches are used it is relatively easy to get large areas which look 'fair', while a lot of small patches are useful in regions where there is a lot of detail. In fact, the size of patches is much easier to alter late in the design than the overall 'run' of the patch boundary directions. If the patch boundaries are poorly selected then patches which are very far from rectangular may occur. In some cases[30] this cannot be avoided, such as triangular patches in corners (Figure 6.16). Triangular patches can be achieved by allowing one side of a patch to degenerate to a point.

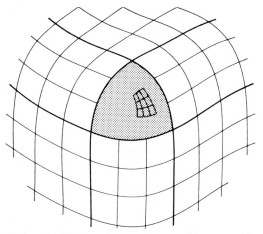

Figure 6.16 Triangular patches are often unavoidable on the corners of sculptured-surfaced objects

Also, special patch equations have been developed both for this case and for polygonal patches with more than four sides. If the shape of a patch is deformed from the rectangular in some other way, such as into an 'L' shape, then the area of that patch should be broken up among smaller patches. Attempting to force a patch equation to accommodate a totally uncongenial boundary is a sure recipe for a wrinkled surface.

An alternative approach to constructing 'awkward' surfaces is the 'carpenter's algorithm'.[22] This starts quite differently from the patches we have been looking at, with a polyhedral representation of the shape. The corners of this polyhedron are truncated, forming new, less acute, corners. These are truncated again and this recursive procedure continues until a sufficiently fine approximation to a smooth surface has been obtained (Figure 6.17). It is not necessarily easy to interface this technique to other surface representations, but under certain conditions the surfaces formed can be shown to be B-spline patches.

Returning to patched surfaces, many designs require that an otherwise large smooth area of surface must be interrupted for functional reasons. For instance, the door panel of a car might require a rebate to accept the door handle. It is possible to break up the patching of a panel to accommodate such a feature but this is usually unwise, as the overall smoothness of the surface can easily be lost. In any case, the interrupting shape may well need a different type of definition from the main surface. In these cases it is necessary to determine the intersections between the two

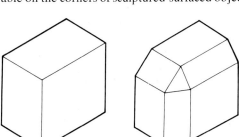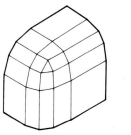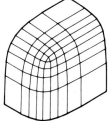

Figure 6.17 The first stages in applying the carpenter's algorithm to three rectangular faces which meet at a square corner. The outside edges of this open polyhedron (shown as thick lines) are actually additional degenerate faces. Such 'double edges' prevent the polyhedron shrinking away from its boundary during subdivision

surfaces. There are severe problems both in calculating intersections and in choosing a representation for the intersection curves once they have been found. Suffice it to say that, between surfaces of the complexity of biparametric patches, numerical techniques are required. The mathematics may be slightly simpler if it is desired to find the intersection between a parametric and an implicit surface: a patch and a plane, for instance. In this case, as we saw in two dimensions in Chapter 2, it is possible to substitute for x, y and z in the implicit equation, and so produce a relatively tractable equation in terms of the patch parameters.

The problem of intersections is compounded when a blend is required at the intersection of two surfaces. If the blend radius is large the best approach may be to repatch the surface to represent the blend explicitly and to deal with any problems resulting from this as they occur. Alternatively, a strictly numerical solution, similar to the blend between ducts mentioned in Chapter 3, could be used. This can fall down when more than two surfaces enter the blend region. In that case, we are left with the possibility of employing a special blend patch[8] with a rather complicated definition which allows it to fulfil boundary conditions specified numerically. Patches may be constructed which exhibit a variation diminishing property, meaning that slope discontinuities at the patch boundaries become smoothed down within the body of the patch surface. The pictures on the back cover illustrate these properties. Unfortunately the computational expense of generating such surfaces is rather severe. Given the many difficulties outlined above it is not surprising that people wishing to manufacture blends between sculptured surfaces often resort to a trick that we shall meet in the next section.

Machining

We have already observed that sculptured surfaces are often used because of the requirements of manufacture, aside from, or in addition to, functional specifications. The sorts of process which need smooth shapes to replicate are casting, forging, injection moulding and the pressing of panels. Once a master pattern, die, mould or press tool has been made, many components can be manufactured, but a numerically controlled milling machine provides the only means by which the carefully constructed numerical information in a sculptured surface can reliably and accurately be transferred to this master shape. The very accuracy of this process, when compared with traditional techniques, may be a major factor in the initial decision to adopt CAE. It is comforting to know that a component that has performed correctly in a prototype will be replicated exactly in the final product. Mould and patternmakers' (legitimate) licence in the interpretation of drawings can lead to considerable variations in performance and possibly even failure.

If a component is to be machined on an NC machine tool we must produce a path for the cutter to follow. The problems of determining a strategy to machine a sculptured surface are not restricted to the manufacturing phase. We have already mentioned that models in foam or wax are often used to verify a shape, and cutter paths must also be determined for these. When machining soft materials, the program that determines the cutter path may be quite cavalier in terms of the amount of material it expects the tool to remove in a single cut. The same flexibility may be extended to the machining of wooden patterns for casting. If, however, the material is a hard tool steel for, say, a forging die, then the cutter path must be determined with the utmost respect for the technological capabilities of the cutter, or it will break and possibly ruin an expensive workpiece, not to mention the machine tool and its operator. If, again, the cutter path is for some reason to be used to produce the final component rather than a pattern, mould or die, then the efficiency of the cutter path becomes the major issue: it is important to keep cutting at full capacity for as much of the time as possible. In some ways the problems of determining a cutter path are analogous to those of producing a picture. For instance, the parts of a model which are hidden in a picture may be thought of as corresponding to the places inaccessible to the cutter. The technological constraints of the machining process make the determination of a cutter path a much more demanding process.[5]

If the blank, the piece of material from which the component is to be machined, is not much larger than the finished component then a single cutter path may suffice. This *finishing* cutter path comprises a series of movements over the parts of the component which are to be machined such that part of the cutter is in constant contact with the surface defined by the computer model. A finishing cut alone may be adequate when the component blank is a casting or forging nearly in its final shape. More frequently we want to machine a sculptured surface component directly from a block of material which is round, square, or some other convenient stock size very different from the final shape. In this case a *roughing* cutter path must also be specified to remove the bulk of the surplus material.

The simplest way to generate a roughing cutter path is to repeat the finishing cutter path many times, starting a long way from the material surface and gradually moving towards it. This approach has often been used because it is simple, but it is also very inefficient, for the cutter is 'cutting air' during the greater part of the earlier repetitions of its path. Furthermore, the cutting is not even: the depth of cut depends on the slope of the surface with respect to the direction from which the cutter is approaching. It is much better to use a separate roughing strategy that leaves a skin of roughly constant thickness over the entire surface, which can then be removed in a single finishing cut. On difficult materials two roughing steps are recommended: 'hogging', to within 2–5 mm of the surface; and roughing proper, to 1 mm, or even closer where the component is thin-walled and may distort during the final cut. One common roughing strategy, used on the workpiece which appears on the back cover, is to define a number of discrete levels, or cutting depths, and to clear the waste material at each of these in turn. Because the roughing process need not be completely accurate, the regions to be cleared can usefully be determined from numerical data derived from the original surface equations, such as a face model or a mesh of surface points. This allows a single program to determine roughing cutter paths for a variety of algebraically different surface types. Because the regions to be cleared in such a strategy have flat bottoms

we can use square-ended cutters, which are able to remove material much more quickly, and also simple parallel cutter paths like those we used in making 2½D shapes.

In calculating a finishing path the first thing to consider is offsetting. As in two-dimensional milling, the instructions, or part program, which go to the NC machine tool define the movement of some constant point on the cutter, which is conveniently considered as being at its centre of rotation. However, it is of course the periphery of the cutter which will determine the resulting form. Therefore the cutter path must be offset from the material surface. Offsetting is easiest if the cutter has a spherical end, and for this reason ball-nosed

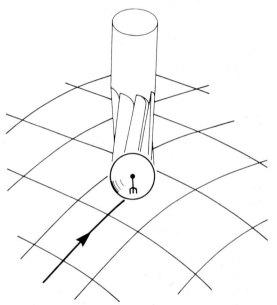

Figure 6.18 The centre of a ball-nosed cutter is offset by a constant distance from a surface so that the periphery of the cutter generates the surface itself

cutters, as they are called, are often used for finishing cuts. The offsetting distance is then independent of the orientation of the cutter to the surface (Figure 6.18). A curve on the surface can be converted into part of the cutter path by moving it out along the appropriate surface normals by a distance equal to the cutter radius (Figure 6.19).

Another matter is the selection of cutter size. Clearly a small cutter will be able to access concave regions denied to larger ones.

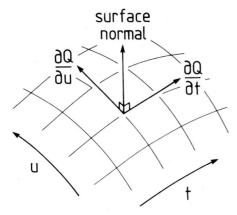

Figure 6.19 The normal to a biparametric surface can be calculated as the vector product (see Figure 4.14) of the partial differentials in the two parametric directions

However, a larger cutter will be able to cut more quickly. It is possible to check that a cutter will not gouge by examining radii of curvature over the surface definition. In practice a cutter is often chosen by rule of thumb, and verification done on a wax model. If there are sharp depressions in the surface it may well be most efficient to use a separate cutter for that region to avoid very slow cutting elsewhere. An unusual Canadian system, called Polyhedral NC,[23] performs both roughing and finishing with a sequence of ball-nosed cutters of decreasing diameter, using each to remove most of the material to which the previous one could not get access.

One of the problems with the ball-nosed cutter is that, when it is generating a surface nearly perpendicular to its axis, cutting is taking place at a very small radius from the axis of rotation and material removal is very slow. Reorientating the workpiece may sometimes be useful, but where a lot of material is to be removed other cutter geometries are commonly used, such as barrel-shaped tools or tools with disc-shaped inserts of carbide set at a considerable distance from the axis (Figure 6.20). The latter form of cutter gives nearly constant surface-cutting speed at all orientations. These tools require somewhat more effort to be put into determining offsets and have large parts of their surface by which cutting cannot be performed at all. In order to keep them correctly orientated, therefore,

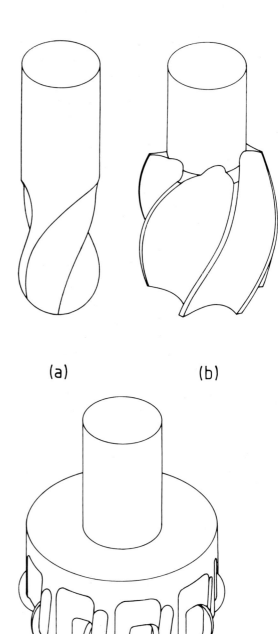

(a)   (b)

(c)

Figure 6.20 Ball-nosed cutters (a) are those most commonly used for finishing sculptured surfaces, but (b) barrel-shaped or (c) disc-insert cutters offer much higher rates of metal removal

their use is commonly associated with powerful machine tools with four, five or six axes of movement all under numerical control.

Having decided what cutter to use and how to generate offsets, it is necessary to decide the path to take over the surface when making the finishing cut. A common and easy strategy is to follow the curves of constant parameter in one direction. Unfortunately the spacing of these may vary considerably, leading to uneven coverage of the surface. Evenly spaced paths across the surface can be generated by programs which make adjustments to the parametric intervals being used as the real spacing of these changes. Other strategies may be quite independent of the parameter system, such as cutting along contour lines.

Whatever the cutting strategy employed, care must be taken that the cutter does not collide with other parts of the workpiece. APT and NMG provide for the definition of *check surfaces*, which are surfaces beyond which cutting must not proceed. This effectively provides a blending facility (Figure 6.21). Because a ball-nosed cutter cannot get into the corner between the surface being cut and the check surface, a radius will be generated. It is considerably simpler to implement the check surface facility than to define the blend explicitly.

All numerical-control machining of complex surfaces leaves a series of ridges or *cusps* of unwanted material between the cutter strokes. They are apparent on one of the workpieces on the back cover. The cusps must be polished out by hand if a smooth surface is required. The back cover also shows a workpiece (laboriously) hand-finished by the author. One of the reasons for using the largest-radius cutter possible is to reduce the height of the cusps, and hence to make finishing easier. If lines of constant parameter are being used as the basis of the cutter path, then cutting in both parametric directions, one after the other, is sometimes performed, on the basis that the 'pips' left after a second cut are easier to remove than ridges. The decisions on this, and on how small a gap to leave between cutter strokes, are essentially economic ones, determined by the relationship between machining and hand-finishing costs, although if too coarse a feed is used final accuracy may suffer. What is important is to ensure that there are no spurious depressions or score marks in the workpiece, such as sometimes occur when a cutter waits, or *dwells*, in one position for a time. These must affect accuracy and, even if this is not critical, are sure to prolong finishing time. Where a dwell mark is possible, sophisticated systems raise the cutter very slightly and leave a 'pip' instead, which can easily be polished out.

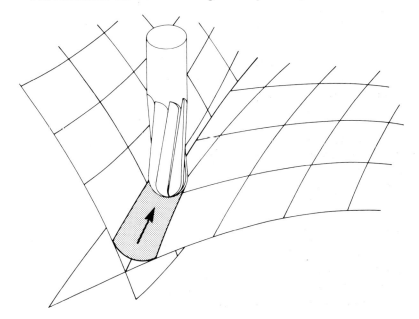

Figure 6.21 Using a round-nosed cutter, a check surface facility automatically provides a blend between intersecting surfaces

7

Solid models

In the shape representations of earlier chapters the main emphasis has been on achieving the required geometry. The user is left to control the representation in detail; in particular, there is no guarantee that the model constructed corresponds to a solid object. A drawing may be nonsense, a face model may have no thickness, and a user of sculptured surfaces may model only the surfaces he wants to machine. The last of these, at least, is certainly a valid CAE activity, so why try to create a model to satisfy more than the immediate needs of a particular production process?

In the past, the vast majority of components were produced by hand or on conventional machine tools. Only very special and sophisticated components might undergo one or two operations involving either computer analysis or numerical control, and each such operation was programmed independently. In many industries there is now much greater reliance on computer analyses, NC machine tools and industrial robots. All these require the provision of geometrical information. If each analysis, NC or robot programming language is separate it is necessary manually to recode parts of a component's geometry into many different formats. For instance, a component such as a compressor blade might require aerofoil data to be entered into a stress analysis and an aerodynamic properties program, the weight of both blade and root to be calculated, a surface representation of the aerofoil suitable for NC to be prepared, and a part program written for machining the root, also by NC. Re-entering data by hand is inefficient, boring (the author has tried it) and, most significantly, prone to mistakes. It is not pleasant to think that the object we are manufacturing might not be the one we stressed.

For these reasons we are going to look in this chapter at complete representations of the shapes of objects. The goal, which has not yet been even nearly achieved, is that all the different phases of a component's design and manufacture can call upon, and if necessary modify, a single representation of the shape of that object and that other forms of geometric data, like NC tool paths, can automatically be derived from it. Because these representations are of whole solid objects we call them *solid models*. (There are a small number of good review papers on this topic, such as refs 3 and 56.)

Representations

A successful scheme for representing solids must be:

(1) Complete and unambiguous, for our goal is to avoid any requirement for human interpretation.
(2) Appropriate to the world of engineering components.
(3) Practical to use with existing computers.

We have already examined representations that fall down on the first of these requirements. An example of a failure on the second count would be a model consisting entirely of spheres, although this is a useful tool in molecular sciences. The third problem occurs with a scheme called *spatial enumeration*. In this case an object is modelled by breaking down the volume it occupies into a mesh of tiny cells and marking these cells as solid or empty as appropriate. To achieve engineering accuracy the number of cells is enormous, and hence both the amount of storage required and processing times are excessive.

There are in fact only two fully distinct solid model representations which have met the above criteria sufficiently well to achieve common currency. They are the *boundary* or graph-based model and the *set-theoretic* or Boolean model (sometimes called CSG, short for computational solid geometry). Although these representations are different they are not exclusive, and are in many ways complementary. It is therefore not uncommon to find that a solid modelling system maintains them both. The boundary model is the one that follows most directly from the shape representations already discussed in this book, so we shall deal with it first.

Boundary models

In Chapter 5 we discussed face models and, among other things, mentioned that some of the processes which we might be interested in performing on them are facilitated if the model contains information as to which faces are joined to which others. If we insert sufficient such pointers we can guarantee the topological consistency of the model simply by checking that everything is linked to everything else. By 'topological consistency' we mean that there are no extra or omitted faces, edges or vertices of the object. The model must obey Euler's rule. For a polyhedron without through holes, this states that the number of edges must always be two less than the sum of the numbers of faces and vertices.

$$F + V = E + 2$$

where F is the number of faces, V is the number of vertices, and E is the number of edges. (A cube, for instance, has 6 faces, 8 vertices and 12 edges: $6 + 8 = 12 + 2$.)

If there are to be pointers between the faces of the object it is unnecessary to store the boundary of each face separately. Indeed, this would introduce a real danger that edges or vertices which were meant to be shared between faces were in fact inconsistent. Faces, edges and vertices are therefore bound into a single data structure with pointers to indicate adjacency and the geometric data recorded only once. The number and nature of pointers need to be sufficient to ensure that we do not revert to the unstructured face model. Most systems overspecify the number of pointers to make programs operating on the structure as fast as possible. One early modeller, GEOMED (Geometric Editor),[4] had enough pointers to avoid any searching operations by a program traversing the model's surface. The pointers that this modeller was the first to use have become something of a standard. They comprise what has been called the *winged-edge* data structure, because it is based on bi-directional pointers between each edge and its adjacent faces (the 'wings'), vertices and edges (Figure 7.1).

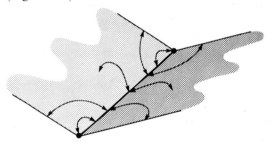

Figure 7.1 The winged-edge data structure provides bi-directional pointers from every edge in a boundary model to its two end vertices, two adjacent faces, and the four other edges that share a face and a vertex with it

Even if topological consistency is ensured, sets of faces may still not be geometrically consistent. In particular a concavity in the object could protrude through the opposite side of the polyhedron. GEOMED only modelled convex polyhedra, and so avoided these problems. This scarcely fulfils the goal of describing a range of engineering components. Ensuring that more complex *boundary models* are geometrically consistent representations of

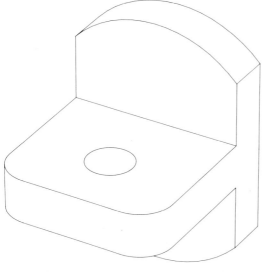

solids is a matter of ensuring that the input process is incapable of producing geometrical anomalies. (In some systems, controlling the model creation process is a partial or complete replacement for purely topological constraints.) The BUILD system[13] was one of the earliest boundary modellers capable of representing moderately complex component geometries, with input and data structure both efficiently controlled to give some confidence in the 'solidity' of the resulting model.

Figure 7.2 was produced by a special routine in BUILD's descendant, ROMULUS, which 'unwraps' the faces of a model onto a flat surface. The resulting layout is very like one of the cardboard cut-out models that used to be printed on the backs of cornflake packets. The labelling of each of the edges to be cut with the

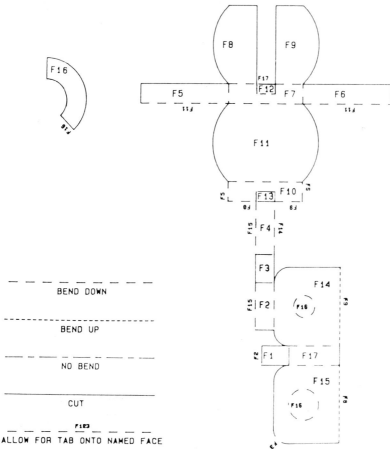

Figure 7.2 It is possible to 'unwrap' a boundary model (top left) and produce a layout of its faces from which a cardboard replica of the shape could be constructed. (Shape Data Ltd)

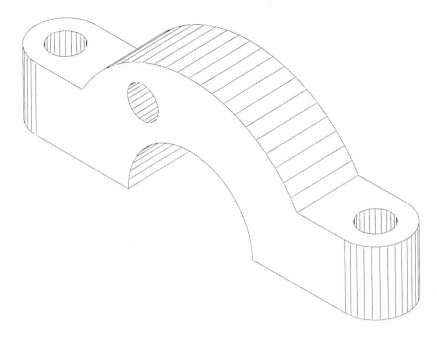

Figure 7.3 A faceted
model. The faceting is
less obvious if the lines
between facets are
omitted (Figure 7.16,
top right view) or in
continuous tone pictures
(Figure 7.11(b), for
example) (Cambridge
Interactive Systems Ltd)

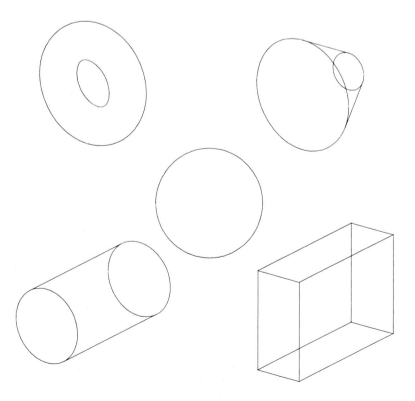

Figure 7.4 Wire frames
of a set of five primitive
solids typical of a solid
modelling system.
(Leeds University
Geometric Modelling
Project)

face with which it mates (corresponding to the tabs on cornflake packet models) is easily derived from a boundary model's data structure. 'Unwrapping' is not a normal part of the operation of ROMULUS but provides a graphic illustration of the structure of boundary models.

Non-planar surfaces

Some solid modelling systems allow only planar surfaces, like face models, and represent curved surfaces approximately, as a number of flat *facets* (Figure 7.3). Using facets vastly reduces the amount of algebra that must be incorporated into the program and there is usually a substantial advantage in speed of computation. However, this approach is quite inadequate in some applications, such as process planning, where analytical knowledge of the non-planar surfaces is essential. Solid modelling systems may have a faceted model as one of a number of representations, for rough calculations and fast picture generation.

If we choose to reject faceting, or require an accurate model in addition to a faceted one, then it is necessary to decide on the surface types that will be allowed. The most generally useful non-planar surfaces in the engineering world are probably the cylinder, cone, torus and sphere, in that order (Figure 7.4). Internal toroidal shapes, it should be explained, are generated in profusion by using radiused cutters on a lathe. It so happens that three of these surfaces, the cylinder, cone and sphere, are examples of a set of surfaces called *quadrics* which have the general implicit equation:

$$ax^2 + by^2 + cz^2 + dxy + exz + fyz + gx + hy + jz + k = 0$$

The torus has a quartic equation.

If we wish to include cylindrical, conical, toroidal and spherical surfaces on our model, and cylindrical surfaces are a bare minimum for any system to claim to be orientated towards mechanical components, then it is not sufficient simply to associate the appropriate surface equation with each face. It is also necessary to represent curved edges. This is a major headache of the boundary model

approach. A cylinder meeting a plane perpendicular to its axis will generate a circular edge. If the plane is at an angle the edge will be elliptical. If, however, the cylinder meets another cylindrical face then the edge does not lie in a plane and its algebra is much more complicated (Figure 7.5). In general, obtaining the intersections between curved surfaces involves both algebraic and numerical difficulties,[43] and an alternative that is often taken is to represent edges approximately, most simply by a number of straight line segments. We have already come across similar but greater difficulties with sculptured surface intersections.

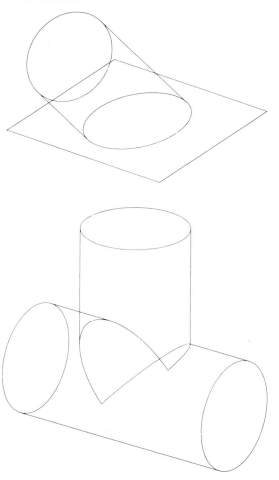

Figure 7.5 An elliptical edge (top) is created by the intersection of a cylinder and a plane. A cylinder-cylinder intersection (above) is much more complicated. (Leeds University Geometric Modelling Project)

Set-theoretic models

Set-theoretic models are based on the idea of defining a complex object as a combination of several simpler objects. We may ensure that the result of the definition is a solid by starting with simple objects that are themselves solids and using methods of combination which ensure that the property of solidity is transferred from the constituents to the resulting object. These methods of combination are actually the well-known operators of set theory: union, difference and intersection. The union operator may be roughly considered to correspond to addition and the difference operator to subtraction. Intersection yields the volume common to the two objects being combined. Figure 7.6 shows the effect of the three operators in combining two blocks and should make their function clear. In theoretical terms, we are considering the simple shapes as *sets* of points and performing the operations on points considered as *members* of the sets being combined.

To build up a complex solid in this way some initial simple shapes, called *primitives*, are necessary. Before primitives are combined, copies, or instances, of appropriate sizes must be placed at the appropriate locations in space. (This instancing process was mentioned in Chapter 5 as a method of constructing large face models, but in that case no subsequent combination takes place.) The range of different shaped primitives that is available determines the range of final shapes that can be produced. Some early modellers also restricted the primitives to certain angular alignments (actually, parallel to the coordinate axes) and this further restricts the final shapes attainable. The number of different types of shape that can be constructed is sometimes called the *domain* of the modeller.

The primitives of a system may be a number of different shaped bricks, such as those shown in Figure 7.4. Alternatively, the conceptually more difficult *half-spaces* may be used. These are single surfaces that have one side marked as solid. They may be semi-infinite, such as the plane, cone or cylinder, or finite, such as the sphere or torus. Some systems use the structure present in primitives to assist internal operations. In others, the user is presented with primitives but these are decomposed into half-spaces internally. Half-spaces are dangerous things for the user to be able to get hold of

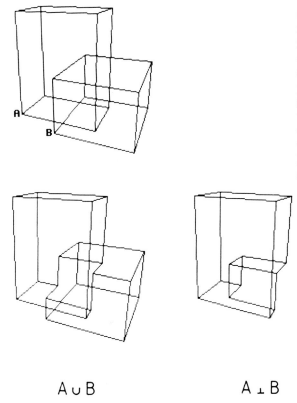

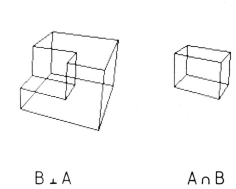

A ∪ B   A ⊥ B   B ⊥ A   A ∩ B

Figure 7.6 The effects of the three set-theoretic operators in combining two blocks displayed as wire frames in perspective projection. (This figure was computed on a BBC Micro, showing that a large machine is not essential for very simple solid modelling)

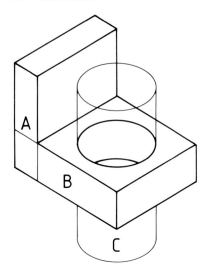

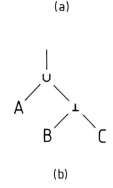

$$A \cup (B \perp C)$$

(a)

(b)

Figure 7.7 A set-theoretic model can be (a) written as a line of algebra or (b) drawn as a tree structure

for he can easily build semi-infinite objects, which usually mean trouble. On the other hand, direct access to half-spaces can often allow the skilled user to construct objects using many fewer elements than with pre-combined primitives, with resulting economies in processing.

After a construction has been built up from the system's primitives, or half-spaces, this may itself be used as the basis of further combinations. Thus an entire set-theoretic model has the form of a tree where the root, which is the whole model, is formed as a combination of its sons. These are formed from their own sons, down to the leaves of the tree which are the primitives. This tree may be written as such, or alternatively as a piece of set-theoretic algebra (Figure 7.7).

Comparing boundary and set-theoretic models

Of the two solid model structures that have been described, the boundary model has been far more frequently implemented. As we shall shortly see, the creation of models of both types may use operations based on the set-theoretic operators, so it is not always obvious to the user which sort of modelling system he is using. In any case, as we have already said, both representations are implemented in some systems. (A 'pure' set-theoretic system is a rarity. TIPS (Technical

Information Processing System)[50] is the best-known example.) The boundary model can be derived relatively easily from the set-theoretic model. We start at the leaves of the operator tree and form the boundary models of the combinations of two primitives. These sub-models are in turn combined until the final boundary model emerges at the root of the tree. This is not, in practice, quite as simple as it sounds, but converting a boundary model to a set-theoretic representation is far more

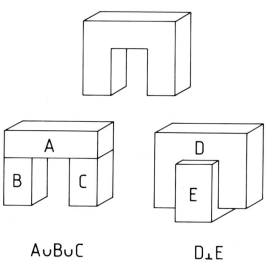

$$A \cup B \cup C \qquad\qquad D \perp E$$

Figure 7.8 These two ways to construct an arch illustrate that an object does not have a unique set-theoretic representation

difficult and as yet a program to do it has not been written. We can be sure that any such program would need to choose from among many possible set-theoretic representations. It is easy to show (Figure 7.8) that a set-theoretic model is not a unique representation of a given object.

Boundary models have clear similarities to face models, and existing computer graphics techniques have readily been adapted to draw them. The accessibility of bounded faces in the boundary model also facilitates the simpler sorts of analysis program, because the information about each face is *localized*. To calculate the surface area of a boundary model, for instance, it is only necessary to add the areas of all the faces together. The set-theoretic model is certainly not localized in that way and its advantages are less obvious. They are mainly in the relative numerical stability, and hence ease of programming, of certain operations. For example, if we have any solid representation, it is reasonable to expect that we might be able to determine whether a given point in space is inside or outside the object that is being modelled. This operation is basic to the construction and use of solid models. It is often called a *membership test* (Figure 7.9).[64] With a boundary model it is necessary to generate a line, or 'ray', from that point to infinity, and then to check all the faces of the model to see how many times the ray intersects them. Numerical problems occur if the ray happens to pass through (or near, allowing for the accuracy of the computer) an edge or vertex. A new ray must be generated, the test repeated, and so on. The set-theoretic membership test, on the other hand, is very simple. The point is simply tested against all the primitives that comprise the solid. Then, as it were 'replaying' the construction of the solid from the primitives, we decide whether the point is in the object by seeing whether it is in the sub-objects which make up the object, taking account of the operators relating them.

In these approaches to the membership test it is necessary to consult every face of the boundary model, and every primitive in the set-theoretic model. The localization of the faces of the former is of little assistance. Tests which require all parts of a model to be examined will obviously be slow when large

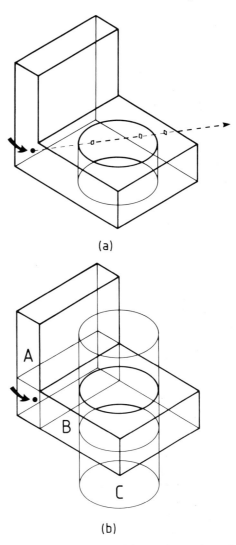

(a)

(b)

Figure 7.9 A membership test determines whether a point is inside or outside a solid model. With a boundary model, a ray must be generated and compared with all the faces of the model. Whether the number of intersections between the ray and the faces is even or odd indicates the status of the point. In this case, there are an odd number of intersections (three), from which we can deduce that the point is inside the object. With a set-theoretic model we can compare the point with each primitive separately and combine these results. In this case, the point is inside blocks A and B, but outside the cylinder C. Recall (Figure 7.7) that the object is represented by the set-theoretic expression A ∪ (B ⊥ C). If the point is inside B and outside C, it must be inside (B⊥C). If it is inside A and inside (B⊥C) it must be inside the whole model

models are under consideration. A common way to try to make things faster is to use boxing tests, which were mentioned in Chapter 5. In solid modelling, three-dimensional boxes—cuboids (or sometimes spheres)—are constructed around each primitive in a set-theoretic model, or each face in a boundary model. These boxes are compared before embarking on a detailed comparison of their contents. Just as in two dimensions, this speeds things up but does not remedy the rate at which computations become longer with complexity. The author has experimented with an alternative technique of breaking up the space which a set-theoretic model occupies into sub-spaces. After this division each sub-space ends up containing a piece of the original model which is applicable to that volume alone[75] (Figure 7.10). (This technique has the immediate advantage of being applicable to half-spaces, which boxing tests are not.) A membership test then reduces to determining the sub-space in which the point of interest lies and comparing the point with the relevant small sub-model. The time required to perform a membership test in this way grows more slowly than model complexity. In effect this approach achieves a

localization of the set-theoretic approach without sacrificing its numerical stability. Of course, this *spatial* localization is very different from the *structural* localization in a boundary model, and has different properties.

Additional features

In addition to the geometry of a component or assembly there are other attributes which solid modellers should be able to represent. It is often useful to be able to attach additional information to surfaces, such as non-numeric labels for the user's convenience, colours for display, or surface finishes or textures. For instance, it would be difficult (on today's systems), and probably rather pointless, to model a knurled surface by modelling each ridge. Giving the entire face the attribute 'knurled' is considerably more practical. It is also possible in a boundary model to attach labels of this sort to an edge: specifying, for example, that it should be deburred or chamfered. This technique has its limitations. An appreciable chamfer or bevel can drastically alter the topology of the shape and make nonsense of the model itself.

A more taxing activity is attaching tolerance information to models. Like engineering drawings, models should be capable of representing a range of slightly different components which are acceptable for a given purpose—'in tolerance'. This problem has proved to be a rather difficult one and the position is not helped by vagueness in the relevant standards, and engineers' somewhat intuitive approach to tolerancing. Tolerances on dimensional information were handled quite convincingly by the early PADL-1 system[65] (PADL stands for Part and Assembly Description Language)—but only within a very limited range of geometries. So-called geometrical tolerances, of form rather than dimension, are still a matter for research.[37,57]

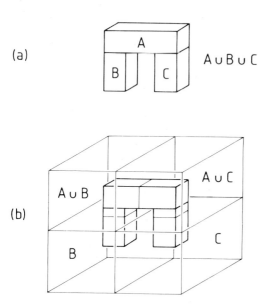

Figure 7.10 An arch is (a) represented by the union of three blocks. The space in which the model lies can be divided (b), giving four sub-models, each of which is simpler than the original single model

Creating solid models

It is by no means the case that all solid models are constructed by people. One use for solid models is in deciding the accuracy of a proposed cutter path on an NC machine tool.[67]

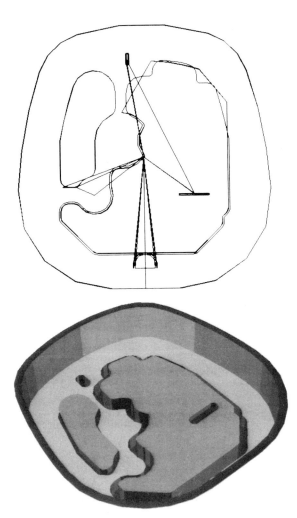

Figure 7.11 A cutter patch for machining a mould for an electric plug can be verified (top) by plotting the path of the cutter centre line, but this picture is difficult to interpret. An alternative (above) is to create a solid model of the mould by subtracting models of each cutter movement from a model of the blank. (Cutter path data from Delta Computer Aided Engineering Ltd)

The volumes swept by the cutter movements are converted to combinations of primitives and differenced from a model of the component blank. The resulting model indicates the shape that would result from the given cutter path (Figure 7.11) and hence its accuracy can be verified.

At the moment, however, people and not programs are responsible for the creation of most solid models, and it is important that the representations chosen should be compatible with a reasonably acceptable method for creating models. Some modelling systems of the boundary type provide *Euler operators*.[45] These comprise ways of adding to a polyhedron without violating Euler's law. While of theoretical interest, these operators are quite alien to the prospective engineering user. However, a similar technique is employed in some systems to make small changes to an almost completed boundary model, in order to add detailed features such as bevels. This process, often called *tweaking*, can be a quick way to introduce details which would otherwise require a disproportionate amount of work. However, the use of Euler operators only guarantees that the resulting model obeys Euler's rule, and we have already stated that this is not the same as ensuring that it represents a solid. Using tweaking, responsibility for the validity of the model reverts to the user.

Other early boundary modellers, such as BUILD, offered the more acceptable concept of 'gluing' objects together. Provided that they met at a common face, pieces of model could be joined into a common structure. Somewhat less obviously, 'negative' objects could be glued to the inside of positive ones to constitute holes. These gluing operators are simply restricted versions of the set-theoretic operators we have already mentioned. Gluing is simpler to implement in boundary modellers, because only the coincident faces of the sub-models being combined have to be cut and linked into the combined structure. By writing a program to undertake a degree of searching, the full set-theoretic operations can be implemented between boundary sub-models. Every face, edge and vertex of each of the two models being combined is examined in respect of the other model, the pieces of structure that are no longer required are discarded and the structure reassembled. This is the process that we have already met in the conversion of set-theoretic to boundary models.

Set-theoretic input languages

The most straightforward way to provide the user with set-theoretic operations is in the form of an input language. Such languages may, as we shall see, have a similar appearance to conventional programming languages and are thus easily learned by people familiar with computer programming. The translation of language input can lean heavily on existing program compilation techniques and no special input hardware is needed. Set-theoretic input languages have three main components:

(1) *Objects* include the primitives supplied by the system, and also new objects created by the user and named by him like variables in a normal programming language. The primitives may be of unit size, or instantiated with the dimensions required.

(2) The set-theoretic *operators*—union, difference and intersection—must be provided to combine objects.

(3) *Transformations* are necessary, so that primitives and constructs can be moved into position before being combined. The translation and rotation operators are both usual, unless the latter is omitted because of a limit on the domain of the modeller. If only unit primitives are supplied, scaling is also essential.

Each line of an input description normally looks like a line from an ordinary programming language, with the name of the object that is being defined appearing to the left of an equals sign and an algebraic combination of primitives, sub-objects and operators to its right. In a set-theoretic system each of these lines of code is translated into a piece of the resulting operator tree. With a boundary modeller, on the other hand, each line is an instruction to the system and results in the creation of a new boundary sub-model.

A hypothetical and very simple language (which leans heavily on PADL-1[65]) might allow two primitives. One could be a rectangular block with its edges parallel to the coordinate axes, which might be instantiated by a line of the form

OBJECT1 = **BLOCK** (X, Y, Z)

where X, Y and Z specify the lengths of the block in the corresponding directions. The second primitive could be a cylinder, where

OBJECT = **ZCYL** (D, L)

creates a cylinder of diameter D and length L, with its axis parallel to the Z axis. (**XCYL** and **YCYL** might also be defined but we do not require them here.) An instantiated primitive is positioned at the origin, and a shift transformation is required to move it into position. Shifting might take the form:

OBJECT2 = **SHIFT** (OBJECT1, DX, DY, DZ)

This creates a new object shifted by DX, DY and DZ from the position of the original object. Finally, the set-theoretic operators could be made available in lines like:

OBJECT3 = OBJECT1 **UNION** OBJECT2

Figure 7.12 shows the model of Figure 7.7 with primitives labelled and the coordinate axes drawn. Using our hypothetical language,

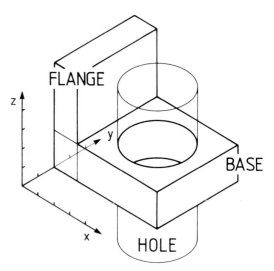

Figure 7.12 The components of the model of Figure 7.7 are named, and an origin and coordinate axes are specified, to show how this component could be constructed using an input language (see text)

we could describe this shape in the following way:

BASE = **BLOCK** (6.5, 5, 2)
BASE = **SHIFT** (BASE, 0, 2, 0)
FLANGE = **BLOCK** (1.5, 5, 5.5)
FLANGE = **SHIFT** (FLANGE, 0, 2, 0)
HOLE = **ZCYL** (4.5, 8)
HOLE = **SHIFT** (HOLE, 4, 4.5, −3)

LSHAPE = BASE **UNION** FLANGE
OBJECT = LSHAPE **DIFFERENCE** HOLE

In addition to these basic facilities, input languages may have statements to specify attributes of parts of a model, from simple things like colours to data for a tolerancing scheme.

It is also possible to combine shape definition statements with conventional algebraic programming statements in a consistent manner. This yields an extremely useful facility of language input, the *parameterized model*. Instead of using numerical constants for instantiation and transformation values, variables are introduced. By relating these together the shape of a part may be made to hinge on a number of characteristic variables, or parameters. Thus a whole set of similar objects of different sizes may be constructed from a single parametric definition. For instance, suppose that a certain type of washer always has an outside diameter that is twice its inside diameter. The model definition

INCYL = **ZCYL** (DIAM, THICK)
OUTCYL = **ZCYL** (2 × DIAM, THICK)
WASHER = OUTCYL, **DIFFERENCE**, INCYL

can generate any washer in the set (Figure 7.13), provided only that values for the parameters DIAM (diameter) and THICK (thickness) are supplied. Such washers may then be created in profusion for use in a model of a large assembly. This technique has the same advantages, both to the user and to his organization, as the parameterized symbols used in draughting systems.

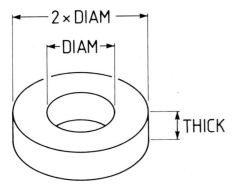

Figure 7.13 The dimensions of a washer labelled to provide a simple example of a parameterized object (see text)

Graphical input techniques

While language input offers a number of powerful facilities, engineers and draughtsmen who are already familiar with graphical methods have, not surprisingly, been found to be unenthusiastic about the idea of a language for shape. A number of graphical input techniques have therefore been developed to offer something more akin to existing design methods, while avoiding trying to interpret an actual engineering drawing.

In Chapter 5 (Figure 5.5) we saw how face models could be generated from two-dimensional sketches. Most graphical input techniques in solid modelling are based on the same idea, but tidied up to ensure that the shapes generated are always solids. In this context the process is often called *sweeping*. (Sweeping was recommended as an internal model structure by an early ANSII standard on

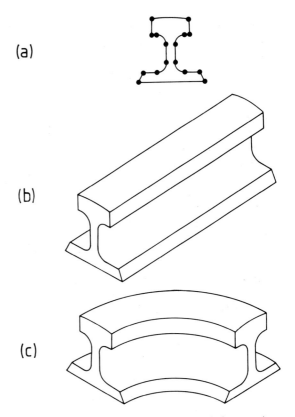

Figure 7.14 A profile can form the basis for creating (a) an extruded volume or (b) part of a solid of revolution (compare Figure 5.5)

modelling,[38] but this never really got off the ground.) A profile is moved along some path in space, generating a volume deemed to be that swept by the area inside the profile. Choosing different paths potentially allows many curious shapes to be created, but the sweep operations commonly implemented are those that we have already seen, which create 'extrusions' and solids of revolution (Figure 7.14). The simple models created by sweeping can subsequently be manipulated with a language like any other primitive or sub-object. It is apparent that even a relatively crude facility of this sort makes easy the construction of a number of shapes that would be puzzling to specify directly as combinations of primitive solids (Figure 7.15).

More elaborate graphical input schemes have been devised which do not require the subsequent use of a language, such as the one used in the MEDUSA system (Figure 7.16). The area of the display screen is divided up into separate views, like a drawing, and curves created in one view are swept through distances or around centre lines specified in other views. This is conceptually rather complicated but powerful in operation, especially as it

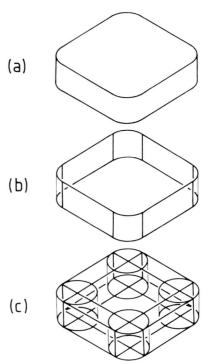

Figure 7.15 A very simple 'extruded' shape (a) can easily be described (b) as a boundary model, but constructing the same object set-theoretically (c) is more complicated

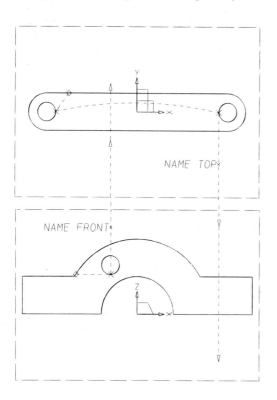

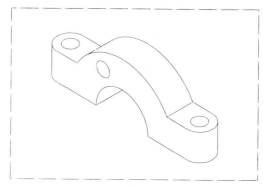

MAKE BRACKET = TOP * FRONT

Figure 7.16 An entirely graphical way to construct models is provided by the MEDUSA system. (Cambridge Interactive Systems Ltd)

allows the user's attention to remain on a single display screen.

It is relatively easy to interpret sweep input into a boundary model. In the case of an 'extrusion', for instance, the contour which the user draws becomes the boundary of the end faces of the resulting object, and each line or arc on the contour also generates a simple planar or cylindrical face on the side of the object. Rotational sweep operations are no more difficult to process. For set-theoretic modellers, however, it is necessary to go 'backwards' and decide what combination of primitives would produce the desired volume. If only planar faces are allowed, it turns out that there is an algorithm to do this which produces as compact a model as possible.[66] Where other types of surface are involved there is a more difficult problem which has as yet received little attention.

Applications of solid modelling systems

The completeness of solid models potentially allows programs to use them without constant guidance. Of course, processes which require additions to basic shape data, such as tolerances, must operate on models which contain that information. It was at one time widely held that the mere existence of a complete shape representation would allow many programs to be developed for engineering applications without further ado. In practice, it has been found that a few relatively simple processes, such as producing pictures or calculating volume properties, are easy to implement once models are available. Attempts to program others, such as NC cutter path generation, have only been successful for models of very restricted domain, or the algorithms have been so inefficient that only very small models can be processed. Many commercial systems have bypassed these difficulties by continuing to use interactive techniques. In particular, solid models are frequently used as a source of data for draughting systems.

Pictures

Producing some form of picture is without exception the first process to be programmed in the development of any new solid modelling system. Pictures are essential in order to verify object definitions and hence to debug the modeller itself. Wire frames may be produced trivially from boundary models simply by plotting all the edges, as in Figure 7.4. A lot has already been said about more realistic pictures in Chapter 5. Boundary models may easily be converted into face models to use those well-established techniques. Alternatively, special picture-generating programs may be written to exploit the extra structure available in a boundary model, and which are also capable of dealing with curved surfaces directly. Figure 7.17 shows a variety of types of line drawing produced from a single model using hidden-line elimination and hatching techniques.

Because of the engineering applications of modelling, there has been some effort put into the generation of engineering drawings from models. There is no great problem in producing the correct views for the component outlines. What is not so easy is to write a program which will automatically add the dimensioning and notation that is usual in drawings, let alone 'scrap views' and other aids to understanding that draughtsmen habitually employ. The pioneer PADL-1 system[65] had dimensioning, and tolerance information too, but the layout could at best be described as stylized. This is one of the processes where an interactive approach, interfacing to a draughting system, is preferred in present-day commercial systems.

Most techniques for obtaining pictures from set-theoretic models involve conversion to boundary models, or processes which are very similar. However, a rather different version of the technique of ray-casting, which was mentioned in Chapter 5, is capable of producing continuous tone pictures from set-theoretic models directly.[32,60] (Of course, ray-casting can be used to produce pictures from boundary models, in a similar manner to face models.) As before, a large number of rays are generated, each one of which corresponds to the viewer's line of sight 'through' a pixel in the display. However, each ray is then compared with every primitive, rather than each face, in the model and any intersections are found. Unlike ray-casting into a face model it is not

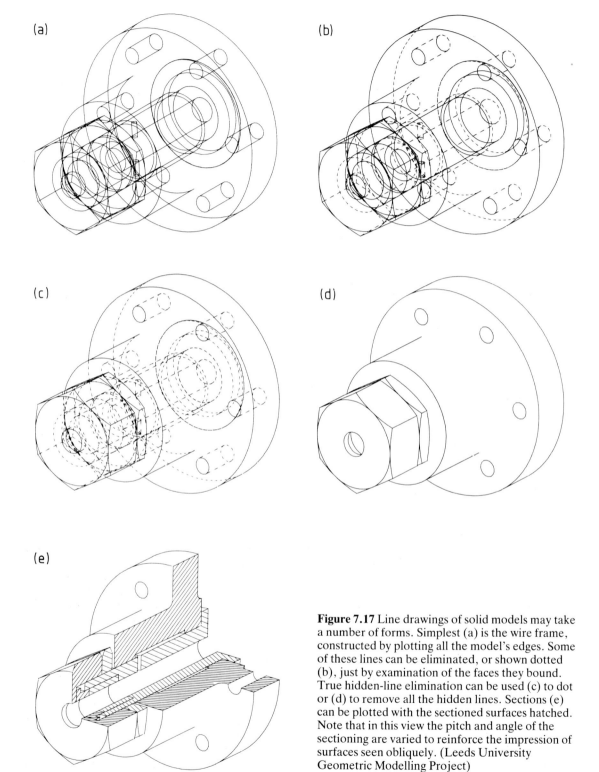

(a)

(b)

(c)

(d)

(e)

Figure 7.17 Line drawings of solid models may take a number of forms. Simplest (a) is the wire frame, constructed by plotting all the model's edges. Some of these lines can be eliminated, or shown dotted (b), just by examination of the faces they bound. True hidden-line elimination can be used (c) to dot or (d) to remove all the hidden lines. Sections (e) can be plotted with the sectioned surfaces hatched. Note that in this view the pitch and angle of the sectioning are varied to reinforce the impression of surfaces seen obliquely. (Leeds University Geometric Modelling Project)

certain that the first, or indeed any, intersection point is actually on the surface of the model. However, the list of intersections with each primitive divides the ray into segments which are inside or outside that primitive, and these lists may be combined using the set-theoretic description of the whole model. The result is a list of intersections with the ray that *do* correspond to real surface on the model, and the nearest of these to the viewer is used to determine the pixel colour, as before. (This is effectively yet another version of the process of set-theoretic to boundary model conversion, but this time considerably simplified by taking place in one dimension.) Computation times for this technique are certainly no better than for ray-casting into a face model, but using a spatially localized model improves matters considerably. The ray is compared first with the division structure and only then with the sub-models in the sub-spaces through which the ray passes. This technique allows much more respectable image generation times, and was used to produce Figures 5.15 to 5.17.

The use of sophisticated graphics techniques such as ray-casting does not necessarily imply a desire for the most realistic possible picture. They can also be used to produce pictures which are essentially unrealistic but which convey a lot of information. The front cover provides an example of this approach. The sectioning of the object is unrealistic in the sense that we could only obtain it in reality by scrapping a component. The colouring is clearly artificial but conveys extra information about the component's surfaces, and the lack of shadows is physically inaccurate but makes the picture easier to read and also faster to compute.

The applications of pictures are not even restricted to the generation of a purely passive medium of communication, however informative. Using a cursor or light pen, a picture on a display may be employed as a key to retrieve information about a model. A point indicated on the screen is transformed to a ray in the model space, just as in the ray-casting technique for picture generation. The geometry of, and information attached to, the part of the model struck by the ray can thus be recovered. Further rays may be generated to make measurements of features of the model in a

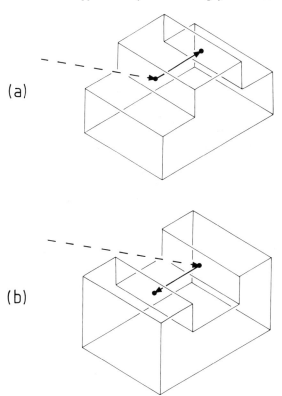

Figure 7.18 Ray-casting can be used to measure models interactively. In these diagrams the dotted lines indicate a ray generated by the user aligning a graphics cursor with a feature of interest on a picture of the model. The solid lines show secondary rays which can make (a) external or (b) internal measurements

way analogous to common hand measuring tools like a micrometer[68] (Figure 7.18). This offers an interesting alternative to trying to display all the dimensional information about a shape at once, with its attendant problems of layout.

Single components

Other than graphics, the applications of solid models may conveniently be divided into processes which are essentially applicable to the model of a single component and those which attempt to simulate the interaction of a number of objects. Probably the simplest process that can be performed on the model of a single component is the determination of its mass properties,[42] including its volume, moments of inertia and principal axes. These calculations can be done without difficulty, except as regards numerical accuracy. On boundary models face integral techniques are used which are analogous to the techniques used to calculate the area of a profile (Figure 3.3). With set-theoretic models it is usual to divide up the volume of the model into cells and to classify these as inside or outside the object by a membership test. A count of the cells inside the object yields the properties required, to an accuracy determined by the fineness of division. Surface areas are very easily obtained from boundary models. With set-theoretic models they can be computed, like the mass properties, using a division technique.

Another interesting use for a single model is in teaching robot vision systems. Instead of presenting the vision system with the actual part to be recognized, it is pre-programmed with pictures computed from a model, and can thus be ready before any parts are actually made. One experimental program[71] has the ability to calculate all the stable orientations of a model. This means that the possible silhouettes that the corresponding part would present to, say, an overhead camera looking at a conveyor belt, can be calculated without having to set up the viewing directions by hand (Figure 7.19).

The generation of meshes for finite-element analysis to determine stress and other distributions has always been a time-consuming process. Deriving the meshes from solid models is possible and the existence of the model is a great help in ensuring that the mesh is self-consistent. Fully automatic mesh generation has been attempted with a certain amount of success,[76] but so far programs written have produced large numbers of simple mesh elements, such as tetrahedra, whereas the trend in finite-element analysis in general is towards smaller numbers of more complex elements. The most satisfactory solution for the moment would seem to be a blend of interaction and automation for different parts of an object, as achieved in Figure 7.20. Automatic techniques are able to deal with regular or non-critical regions without difficulty, leaving the awkward bits for interactive solution.

On the manufacturing side, the most commonly mentioned process is the generation of numerical-control cutter paths. There have been a number of research attempts automatically to derive NC information from solid models (refs 36 and 74, for example). All have been successful in part, but with severe limitations on the range of shapes that could be tackled and long processing times for any but the simplest models. Also, automated approaches may generate cutter paths which, while notionally valid, are not acceptable in the

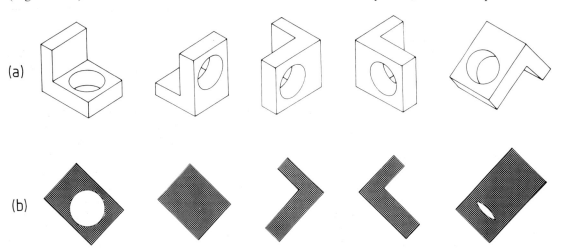

Figure 7.19 If the stable orientations of a component (a) can be calculated from a model, silhouettes (b) can be determined and used to program an industrial vision system

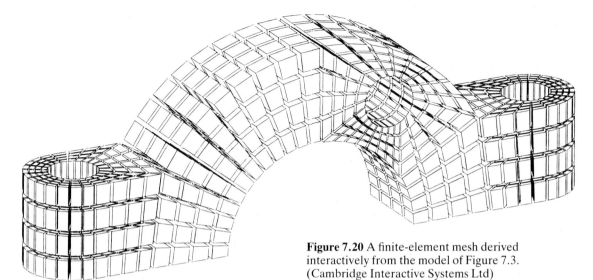

Figure 7.20 A finite-element mesh derived interactively from the model of Figure 7.3. (Cambridge Interactive Systems Ltd)

workshop, just as with 2½D systems. Many commercial solid modellers now have facilities to transfer geometric data into earlier and less sophisticated software such as GNC and APT[15] for the cutter paths to be specified. There has not been much development of manufacturing applications of solid models other than machining, although some work has been done on aspects of injection moulding, forging and casting.[16,69]

Assemblies and workplaces

Up to now, more effort has been put into modelling single components than assemblies. In particular, the ability that solid modelling systems share with draughting systems, to access standard parts and features quickly and thus to encourage maintenance of company standards, has hardly been exploited. The complex geometric interactions which occur between a number of parts provide another useful application of solid modelling. Unwanted interferences between different components may be detected, of which some would not be apparent in an orthographic assembly drawing. This can be done automatically,[12] or by computing and displaying the intersection of the two objects which might interfere (Figure 7.21), or simply by examining pictures computed from an appropriate viewpoint. More

complex interference problems could be tackled, too. For instance, models of hand tools like spanners might be temporarily introduced into an assembly to check that it can be put together. Interactive techniques to probe into assemblies have not yet been well developed.

The modelling of more than one object need not be restricted to assemblies but can be used to simulate an entire workplace and its occupants, human or otherwise. SAMMIE (System for Aiding Man–Machine Interaction Evaluation)[9] consists of a boundary model of the human frame, which is constrained to take up anatomically sensible poses and which can be modified to represent people of different sizes. It can be placed in a model of its environment constructed by gluing polyhedral primitives together. Pictures of the entire scene can be generated and may be used to verify whether a man in that situation would be able to perform the required task (Figure 7.22).

The same techniques have been applied to the modelling of industrial robots.[10] At the moment, most industrial robots are 'taught' the movements they have to perform by someone guiding them around the path they are going to take. In operation, the robot simply replays this path. As more robots are introduced into industry, teaching each robot each job that it is to perform becomes an increasingly large drain on both people's and robots' time. In particular, the necessity for teaching inhibits the

Figure 7.21 This set-theoretic model of a machining cell includes an industrial robot with a workpiece in its gripper. With the robot arm in a particular position, we suspect from a picture of the model (top) that a collision has occurred. The collision volume can be calculated, and superimposed (left) on the original picture (with the component blanked out for clarity)

introduction of robots into small batch manufacturing. The alternative is to program a robot's movements in advance. The very complex geometry involved means that a software system is required which has a knowledge of robot kinematics and dynamics, as well as a model of the robot and the workplace. One of the most important tasks of a robot programming system is to avoid the robot crashing into things, or two 'co-operating' robots crashing into each other. Existing systems compute 'snapshots' of the moving components (like the one shown in Figure 7.23) at a number of points in their trajectory, and test for interference at these points.

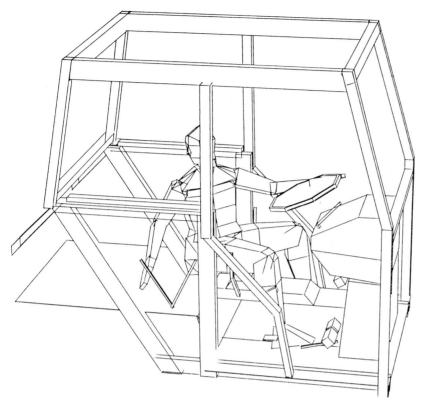

Figure 7.22 A model of a tractor driver in his cab.
(Loughborough University)

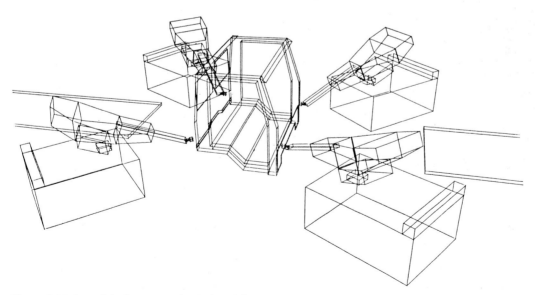

Figure 7.23 A model of co-operating industrial
robots assembling a truck cab. (Loughborough
University)

An alternative is to extend the whole idea of solid models into four-dimensional space by including time. Such an approach has been proposed, using set-theoretic modelling techniques.[14] As one might expect, the storage requirements of four-dimensional models and the time taken by algorithms to operate on them are very considerable, but this should merely encourage us in the development of more efficient solid modelling techniques.

8

Prospects

Commercial systems

In this book there has been little mention of the named computer software systems that embody the various techniques of shape representation. This reticence is not only a reflection of the author's desire to retain some sort of impartiality. There is the much more pressing requirement not to publish a book that seems old-fashioned because the package that was released last month is not in it. Of course, it is impossible to aim to write anything definitive in such a changing field, but the author has tried to mention only those systems that are already classics at the time of writing.

Another reason for not listing systems by name is the very sharp increase in their number, particularly draughting systems and solid modelling systems, available over the last few years. The reason for this is the continuing fast decline in computer hardware prices. Originally most software for computer-aided design and manufacture ran on very large computers, and many people in an organization would use it from separate terminals. The author is just old enough to have recollections of the really bad old days before that, when punched cards went in and drawings and NC tapes appeared a few days later. Hardware was inordinately expensive, and software had to be too, because of the tiny market. Those machines were, in the jargon, mainframes. Since then we have seen simpler and much cheaper minicomputers and microcomputers

appear and then become as powerful as the mainframes of only a few years ago. Increasingly, it is seen as more efficient to provide every user with his own processor, rather than to incur the complexity of connecting a large number of users up to a central machine, which then spends a lot of its expensive time merely deciding what to do next. Unfortunately, however, there are then problems when people want to share information, or someone wishes that they had a large processor available for 'the occasional finite element job'. The two solutions that are popular at the moment are a relatively small number of people, say a dozen, sharing a big 'super-minicomputer' with a 32-bit word length, or roughly the same number of people working on their own microcomputers, linked together and to a central file store by a local area network. Of course, the availability of smaller computers has allowed a large number of smaller organizations and individuals to own just one or two machines and these people are a quite new class of user of CAE.

The cost of other components of a CAE system has also declined. Displays have become very much cheaper, particularly because of the rise of raster-scan, with its use of standard television technology. Despite including major mechanical assemblies, printers and plotters have also fallen dramatically in price. Even the cost of numerical control machine tools (or at least of their controllers) has dropped. Software is subject to the same economies of scale. It is possible to buy a very simple draughting system for a domestic microcomputer for only a few times the cost of a 'space invaders' game for the same machine. Even if you cannot design a gas turbine with such packages, they are probably having a profound effect on the next generation of designers and draughtsmen.

In the old days, a firm would buy a computer because it was suitable for doing the payroll, or at least they had been told it was. The design or production departments might then go shopping for some expensive CAD and CAM packages to run on their very expensive machine. It is now often more logical to select the CAE software that seems the best, which is still quite pricey especially if it is from a supplier who is likely to be able to maintain it (he knows the value of this) and then to buy a suitable computer with the change. One of the messages of this book is that, in the future, the first stage will be to decide on a system which can represent the shape of the product. Application software will come after that and, almost as an afterthought, the machine.

Research

The commercial razzmatazz about CAE gives the impression of a technology in which research has achieved its goals and exploitation is well under way. It is certainly true that the main impetus in CAE has been transferred from academic institutions to firms. This is because many of the people who were most active in recent commercially exploitable research have understandably moved into industry with the very purpose of exploiting it. (The author notes in passing that companies formed by those whose research was the most innovative have largely been the most successful in this field, an observation which contrasts with the common notion of the commercially incompetent academic.) These firms are now large enough to undertake their own, modest, research programmes. They are naturally concerned with finding enhancements and additional applications for the particular shape technology which the firm was formed to exploit, and they have little motivation to encourage developments which would commit

them to major changes in the most basic data structures of their products. One may recollect how some of the companies that had been selling draughting systems were unwilling to consider that solid modelling techniques had anything to offer, and swore by wire frames. Then they started to lose customers and solid modelling programs were produced very quickly. The best software is rarely written in a hurry. While there is little doubt that existing techniques will find wider application, it is also true that successful applications have been much more difficult to achieve than was thought at one time would be the case, and this should prompt the non-partisan observer to look closely at the technology as a whole.

Representations

The academic research work that is still being done on shape technology is also mostly concerned with applications. This reflection of the priorities of the commercial world results from the policy, admirable in itself, of encouraging 'industrial relevance' in research. The only major exception to this state of affairs is a continuing fascination with the mathematics of parametric curves and surfaces. New algebraic results appear monthly, but very little of this work results in systems capable of cutting metal. As a result of all this some people believe that the issue of representations is closed, with the exception of a coherent integration of existing sculptured surface concepts within solid modelling, which can already to some extent be demonstrated.[39] The author thinks differently: he can see room for considerable improvement in three directions.

Firstly, sculptured surfaces: the techniques that were mentioned in Chapters 4 and 6 were all developed before the more structured approach of solid modelling had become common. There seems little reason why the two should be expected to be compatible. In particular it is hard to reconcile set-theoretic modelling techniques with parametric surfaces. These surface types are not in any case particularly suitable for blends, and some implicit blend surfaces have already appeared in experimental implementations (Figure 8.1). There is a danger of systems needing to support three or four different types of

Figure 8.1 A solid model of part of a gear-testing machine produced by an experimental solid modelling system. This model is an entirely set-theoretic combination of shapes defined by implicit equations, including the blends on the casting

sculptured surface, with all the complications that would result. A fundamental rethink of sculptured surface techniques would be preferable.

Secondly, the speed of computation with many shape representations is inadequate for truly interactive working on current computers. Furthermore, this problem becomes dramatically and non-linearly worse as we try to model more complex components and assemblies. Many people suggest that this difficulty will disappear with increasingly fast hardware. Increases in the speed of conventional computer architectures are unlikely to meet demands for performance within the foreseeable future. Two other possibilities exist. One is a basic change in representation

to minimize combinatorial effects. The other is to use unconventional computers with more than one processor running in parallel. In the end, software that avoids combinatorial problems may well split tasks in a way that also facilitates parallel computation.

Thirdly, there are organizational problems with shape information that will also get worse as more and more complex products are modelled. This has led to various attempts to integrate shape descriptions with existing database techniques. Just like the mixing of sculptured surface and solid modelling technology, one or two people have questioned the wisdom of trying to make database techniques that were originally designed for commercial data accept shape information. Their doubts seem to be borne out by the effect on computation times which is usually observed when a shape representation system is made to draw its data from a conventional database. There is room for fundamental work on all three of these topics. When and where it will take place is a different matter.

Input

Almost the sole criterion for choosing a particular draughting system is the ease with which data can be entered and modified. More complex software tends to require more effort in preparing data, although the user is eventually rewarded with a more complete, and hopefully more useful, shape model. This does not mean that we should turn a blind eye to the defects in the user interfaces of sculptured surface and solid modelling programs. In both cases the problem is really that of trying to design in three dimensions on a two-dimensional display. One way forward is to look for developments in displays themselves. There have been experiments with three-dimensional displays but so far they rely on a lot of mechanical hardware, such as rotating or vibrating mirrors, and these displays can only plot vectors. Alternatives include various forms of stereoscopic display. Most of these special graphics devices have the disadvantage of imposing some physical restraints on the user. Three-dimensional displays would seem particularly valuable for the tricky task of specifying control points for sculptured surfaces. For solid models and instantiation systems, on the other hand, language input is well-established but not too popular. We have already mentioned that it has not yet proved possible to program computers to understand engineering drawings. Attacks on this problem have at least led to systems capable of interpreting simple sketches, consisting of a number of views, and it is reasonable to expect input handling along these lines to be more popular with the 'traditional' engineer and draughtsman.

Better input techniques will make it easier for the designer to be innovative in the shapes that he creates. However, a designer's freedom is not always appreciated by his firm, which is probably trying to cut costs by controlling variation in bought-out components and tooling. It is of course possible to build a system which constrains the designer to use standards, but this is unlikely to achieve harmony between man and machine, or indeed man and manager. A more productive approach is to ensure that the system makes standard components and features, such as keyways, very easy to call up. If he does not have to wade through a massive design standards manual a designer may well be grateful to have some of the small decisions, choosing the exact thickness of a washer for instance, taken out of his hands. If he is thus persuaded to opt for a standard component or feature, the system should be able to reward him by relieving him of the work of creating that part of the model. Some catalogue information is already available in computerized form, and we may soon expect that the manufacturer of, say, fastening devices will be expected to provide computer models of the shapes of his products before he can hope to sell the products themselves.

Applications

The only application that is universal to all shape description techniques is the generation of pictures. This is well developed for the reason given earlier: pictures are needed to verify the shape model inside the computer. Engineers have not always been receptive to the more sophisticated graphics techniques. Up until quite recently there was little enthusiasm for colour displays. The limitations of earlier techniques of drawing reproduction had made colour impossible, and a tradition of coping with this situation, even identifying it with 'real' engineering, had arisen. Now colour displays have become commonplace and colour hardcopy devices are improving rapidly. One or two people were persuaded to risk their reputations and try these new ideas in fields where colour would obviously be helpful: for instance in interactive finite element mesh generation and on jig and tool drawings, where the component to be jigged is often traditionally drawn in colour. Whether the enthusiasm is about clarity of presentation, or a 'high-tech' image, is open to question. The image may well be what sells the product, in any case.

The only other applications which are commonly performed quite automatically are the calculations of area and, where appropriate, volume properties. There are other useful processes which are simply *deriving* information from a representation in a straightforward way, such as calculating the silhouette of a shape. Tasks like this are not intrinsically difficult to program provided that the shape model contains enough information. Other desirable applications require the *synthesis* of a new structure from the object's shape. Examples are the generation of finite element meshes and NC cutter paths. At the moment, as we have already seen, these processes are carried out with manual assistance, often including the translation of shape information from a more to a less complete representation for which an interactive interface already exists. We may expect this approach to persist in the future, but with new application programs which are still interactive but use the more complete component model directly.

The full automation of applications which require some synthesis has been shown to be a tricky business. Probably the best results so far have been achieved for finite element mesh generation. There has been a lot of work, but not much progress, in producing cutter paths. Other potential developments, the automatic design of jigs and fixtures for instance, promise to be no easier. Even more complex problems are raised when we try to describe whole assemblies and machines, instead of merely single components. As the size and speed of both hardware and software increase, these sorts of application will receive more attention. There are already demands to model the interaction of many objects, arising out of industrial robotics and flexible manufacturing systems technologies. Just as with single objects, a few simple problems such as determining intersections between objects have been solved. The potential problems of synthesis are enormous. Deciding, for instance, how a machine should be assembled is in some way similar to the toolpath generation problem, but vastly compounded because both 'tool' and 'workpiece' are now of arbitrary shape. Work is under way in these areas,[44] but the near future will lie with interactive techniques.

If we are to persist in searching for automated solutions, then one very possibly relevant piece of new technology is the *expert system*. This is a type of program which is capable of making deductions from an organized body of information with which it is supplied. This information, or knowledge, is acquired from human experts, like whom the system is supposed to behave. Programs have been written which out-perform the experts themselves, but only in very narrow and well-defined subject areas. An expert system[21] has already been written for the planning of machining processes, but only after the geometric information has been digested by a human process planner. The system only accepts logical arrangements of features expressed as text, not a shape model. However, other work[41] has managed automatically to generate a parts classification (such as the Opitz code) from solid models. This extraction of qualitative geometric data could provide shape information in a way today's expert systems can fit into their framework of logical relations. In the future we may see programs capable of direct geometric reasoning. They would need some rather clever way to avoid indigestion caused by the number of different ways one can look at a single shape: should an arch be two pillars and a lintel, or a block with a slot in its base? (We have already looked at this particular example in Figure 7.8.) A little caution is advised by the example of machine algebra: getting computers to solve equations. The expert system type of approach produced only very modest results over several years. Recently, new deterministic algorithms have been devised which are much more reliable and efficient. Machine algebra, like geometry, is a field bedevilled by the number of combinations in which things can occur. Perhaps a turning to the expert system approach would actually signal a failure to solve these problems at their roots.

Conclusion

There seems little doubt that the representation of shape information in a computer will remain one of the fundamental technologies of computer-aided engineering. It has only recently identified itself, and should grow both by development and also by the coalescing and merging of techniques which were hitherto embedded in programs with very different goals. The systems based on this shape technology can be seen as taking engineering in two different ways. On the one hand there is the basis for a quickening of the pace of many aspects of design and manufacture: in some cases, such as the numerical control machine, there is a complete deskilling, while in others, like draughting, the reverse occurs and work takes on a hectic pace. On the other hand, processes like finite element analysis may allow us to evaluate designs and thoughtfully to look at many alternatives. While the need for cheapness and therefore speed is apparent, the final test of CAE will be as an information amplifier rather than accelerator. Does it assist us to make the best use of our resources, not merely to consume them more and more quickly?

Realism about, and even enthusiasm to solve, the problems of the planet need not imply a rejection of technology pursued for its own sake. A video game or a radio telescope make few material demands: they handle information. The engineer at his screen may look like, but is not, a video game player, nor is his quest that of the astronomer—to discover the workings of things which already exist. Instead he is examining alternative visions of his own invention which the machine reflects to him. If he appears to dream, it is a dream by which the engineer has always been haunted: the artefact utterly fit for its purpose, but also perfect in its economy of every sort of resource.

References

The following list of books and papers has no pretence to completeness. It has been chosen simply to allow the reader easily to pursue topics from the text. In the case of technical papers, availability has been a major factor in deciding between a number of possible references on a topic. The asterisked references are books and review papers which have a relatively wide coverage and are recommended to those readers wishing to make an organized entry into the extensive literature of shape representation in CAE. These all contain a large number of further references.

1. J.H. AHLBERG, E.N. NILSON and J.L. WALSH (1967), *The theory of splines and their applications*. Academic Press
2. A. APPEL, F.J. ROHLF and A.J. STEIN (1979), 'The haloed line effect for hidden line elimination'. *Computer Graphics*, Vol. 13, No. 2 (Proceedings of the ACM SIGGRAPH 79 Conference, Chicago (US)), pp. 151–7
*3. A. BAER, C. EASTMAN and M. HENRION (1979), 'Geometric modelling: a survey'. *Computer-Aided Design*, Vol. 11, No. 5, pp. 253–72
4. B.G. BAUMGART (1975), 'A polyhedron representation for computer vision'. Proceedings of the (US) National Computer Conference, Anaheim (US), pp. 589–96
5. C. BELL, B. LANDI and M.A. SABIN (1973), 'The programming and use of numerical control to machine sculptured surfaces'. Proceedings of the 14th International Machine Design and Research Conference, Manchester (UK), pp. 233–8
6. P. BÉZIER (1973), 'UNISURF system: principles, programme, language'. In *Computer Languages for Numerical Control*, J. Hatvany (ed), North-Holland (Proceedings of the PROLAMAT 73 Conference, Budapest (Hungary)), pp. 417–26
7. M.S. BLOOR, A. DE PENNINGTON, J.S. SWIFT and J.R. WOODWARK (1976), 'GLADES— a graphical laminar design system'. Proceedings of DECUS Europe Conference, Munich (West Germany), pp. 367–70
8. M.S. BLOOR, A. DE PENNINGTON and J.R. WOODWARK (1978), 'RISP—bridging the gap between conventional surface elements'. Proceedings of CAD–78 Conference, Brighton (UK), pp. 117–8
9. M.C. BONNEY, C.A. BLUNSDEN, K. CASE and J.M. PORTER (1979), 'Man-machine interaction in work systems'. *International Journal of Production Research*, Vol. 17, No. 6, pp. 619–29
10. M.C. BONNEY, P.J. EDWARDS, J.A. GLEAVE, J.L. GREEN, R.J. MARSHALL and Y.F. YONG (1984), 'The simulation of industrial robot systems'. *OMEGA International Journal of Management Science*, Vol. 12, No. 3, pp. 273–81
11. A. BOWYER and J.R. WOODWARK (1983), *A programmer's geometry*. Butterworths
12. J.W. BOYSE (1979), 'Interference detection among solids and surfaces'. *Communications of the ACM*, Vol. 22, No. 1, pp. 3–9
13. I.C. BRAID (1975), 'The synthesis of solids bounded by many faces'. *Communications of the ACM*, Vol. 18, No. 4, pp.209–16
14. S.A. CAMERON (1984), 'Modelling solids in motion'. PhD Thesis, University of Edinburgh (UK)
15. B.T.F. CHAN (1982), 'ROMAPT: a new link between CAD and CAM'. *Computer-Aided Design*, Vol. 14, No. 5, pp. 261–6
16. Y.K. CHAN and W.A. KNIGHT (1980), 'MODCON: a system for the CAM of dies and moulds'. Proceedings of CAD-80 Conference, Brighton (UK), pp. 370–81

17. S.A. COONS and B. HERZOG (1967), 'Surfaces for computer-aided aircraft design'. Proceedings of the AIAA 4th Annual Meeting and Technical Display, Anaheim (US) (AIAA Paper 67–895)

18. K.J. DAVIES (1973), 'GNC—a graphical NC processor'. In *Computer Languages for Numerical Control*, J. Hatvany (ed). North-Holland (Proceedings of the PROLAMAT 73 Conference, Budapest (Hungary)), pp. 51–61

19. A.C. DAY (1972), *FORTRAN techniques*. Cambridge University Press

20. C.J. DATE (1977), *An introduction to database systems*, 2nd edition. Addison-Wesley

21. Y. DESCOTTE and J.C. LATOMBE (1981), 'GARI: A problem solver that plans how to machine mechanical parts'. Proceedings of the IJCAI 81, pp. 766–71, Vancouver (Canada)

22. D.W.H. DOO (1978), 'A subdivision algorithm for smoothing down irregular shaped polyhedrons'. Proceedings of an International Conference on Interactive Techniques in Computer Aided Design, Bologna (Italy), pp. 157–65

23. J.P. DUNCAN and S.G. MAIR (1977), 'The anti-interference features of polyhedral machining'. In *Advances in Computer-Aided Manufacture*, D. McPherson (ed). North Holland (Proceedings of the PROLAMAT 76 Conference, Stirling (UK)), pp. 181–95

*24. I.D. FAUX and M.J. PRATT (1979), *Computational geometry for design and manufacture*. Ellis Horwood

25. J.C. FERGUSON (1964), 'Multivariate curve interpolation'. *Journal of the ACM*, Vol. 11, No. 2, pp. 221–28

26. A.G. FLUTTER and R.N. ROLPH (1976), 'POLY-SURF: an interactive system for the computer-aided design and manufacture of components'. Proceedings of the CAD-76 Conference, London (UK), pp. 150–58

*27. J.D. FOLEY and A. VAN DAM (1982), *Fundamentals of interactive computer graphics*. Addison Wesley

28. A.R. FORREST (1972), 'On Coons and other methods for the representation of curved surfaces'. *Computer Graphics and Image Processing*, Vol. 1, pp. 341–59

29. A.R. FORREST (1972), 'Interactive interpolation and approximation by Bézier polynomials'. *Computer Journal*, Vol. 15, No. 1, pp. 71–9

30. A.R. FORREST (1978), 'A unified approach to geometric modelling'. *Computer Graphics*, Vol. 12, No. 2, pp. 264–9 (Proceedings of the ACM SIGGRAPH Conference, Atlanta (US))

31. A.R. FORREST (1979), 'On the rendering of surfaces'. *Computer Graphics*, Vol. 13, No. 2, pp. 253–9 (Proceedings of the ACM SIGGRAPH 79 Conference, Chicago (US))

32. R. GOLDSTEIN and L. MALIN (1979), '3D modelling with the Synthavision system'. Proceedings of the First Annual Conference on Computer Graphics in CAD/CAM Systems, Cambridge (US), pp. 244–7

33. W.J. GORDON and R.F. RIESENFELD (1974), 'Bernstein-Bézier methods for the computer-aided design of free form curves and surfaces'. *Journal of the ACM*, Vol. 21, No. 2, pp. 293–310

34. T.H. GOSSLING (1976), 'The 'DUCT' system of design for practical objects'. Proceedings of a Conference of the International Federation for the Theory of Machines and Mechanisms on Computer-Aided Design in Mechanical Engineering, Milan (Italy), pp. 305–16

35. H. GOURAUD (1971), 'Continuous shading of curved surfaces'. *IEEE Transactions on Computers*, C-20(6), June, pp. 623–8

36. A.R. GRAYER (1977), 'The automatic production of machined components starting from a stored geometric description'. In *Advances in Computer-Aided Manufacture*, D. McPherson (ed), North Holland (Proceedings of the PROLAMAT 76 Conference, Stirling (UK), pp. 137–5

37. R.C. HILLYARD and I.C. BRAID (1978), 'Characterizing non-ideal shapes in terms of dimensions and tolerances'. *Computer Graphics*, Vol. 12, No. 3, pp. 234–8 (Proceedings of the ACM SIGGRAPH 78 Conference, Atlanta (US))

38. S. HORI (1976), 'Digital representation of physical object shapes'. American National Technical Report, ANSI Subcommittee Y14.26, January

39. G.E.M. JARED and T. VARADY (1984), 'Synthesis of volume modelling and sculptured surfaces in BUILD'. Proceedings of CAD-84, Brighton (UK), pp. 481–95

40. A.R. JOHNSON and D.P. STURGE (1979), 'The DUCT system of design and manufacture for patterns moulds and dies'. Proceedings of the 20th International Machine Tool Design and Research Conference, Birmingham (UK), pp. 17–20

41. L. KYPRIANOU (1980), 'Shape classification in computer-aided design'. PhD Thesis, University of Cambridge (UK)

42. Y.T. LEE and A.A.G. REQUICHA (1982), 'Algorithms for computing the volume and other integral properties of solids. *Communications of the ACM*, Vol. 25, No. 9 (Part 1: pp. 635–41, Part 2: pp. 642–50)

43. J. LEVIN (1976), 'A parametric algorithm for

drawing pictures of solid objects composed of quadric surfaces'. *Communications of the ACM*, Vol. 19, No. 10, pp. 555–63

44. T. LOZANO-PEREZ and M.A. WESLEY (1979), 'An algorithm for planning collision-free paths among polyhedral obstacles'. *Communications of the ACM*, Vol. 22, No. 10, pp. 569–70

45. M.J. MANTYLA and R. SULONEN (1982), 'GWB: a solid modeller with Euler operators'. *IEEE Computer Graphics and Applications*, September, pp. 17–31

46. G. MARKOWSKY and M.A. WESLEY (1980) 'Fleshing out wire frames'. IBM Research Report RC8124

*47. W.M. NEWMAN and R.F. SPROULL (1979), *Principles of interactive computer graphics*, 2nd edition. McGraw-Hill

48. R.G. NEWELL, T.J. SANCHA, R.G. WILLIAMSON and J.O. HILES (1977), 'The design of systems for CAD'. In *CAD Systems*, J.J. Allen (ed), North-Holland (Proceedings of the IFIP Working Conference on CAD Systems, Austin (US), 1976), pp. 121–42

49. H. NOWACKI (1980), 'Curve and surface generation and fairing'. In *Computer Aided Design— Modelling, Systems Engineering, CAD Systems*, J. Encarnacao (ed), Springer-Verlag, pp. 137–76

50. N. OKINO, Y. KAKAZU and H. KUBO (1973), 'TIPS-1: Technical information processing system, for computer-aided design, drawing, and manufacturing'. In *Computer Languages for Numerical Control*, J. Hatvany (ed), North Holland (Proceedings of the PROLAMAT 73 Conference, Budapest (Hungary)), pp. 141–50

51. A.W. OVERHAUSER (1968), 'Analytic definition of curves and surfaces by parabolic blending'. Ford Motor Company Scientific Laboratories Technical Report SL68-40

52. E.S. PAGE and L.B. WILSON (1978), *Information representation and manipulation in a computer*, 2nd edition. Cambridge University Press

53. H. PERSSON (1978), 'NC machining of arbitrarily shaped pockets'. *Computer-Aided Design*, Vol. 10, No. 3, pp. 169–74

54. B.-T. PHONG (1975), 'Illumination for computer-generated pictures'. *Communications of the ACM*, Vol. 18, No. 6, pp. 311–7

55. K. PREISS (1980), 'Constructing the 3-D representation of a plane-faced object from a digitised engineering drawing'. Proceedings of the CAD-80 Conference, Brighton (UK), pp. 257–65

*56. A.A.G. REQUICHA (1980), 'Representations of rigid solids: theory methods and systems'. *ACM Computer Surveys*, Vol. 12, No. 4, pp. 437–64

57. A.A.G. REQUICHA (1983), 'Toward a theory of geometric tolerancing'. *International Journal of Robotics Research*, Vol. 2, No. 4, pp. 45–60

*58. D.F. ROGERS and J.A. ADAMS (1976), *Mathematical elements for computer graphics*. McGraw Hill

59. D.T. ROSS (1959), 'The design and use of the APT language for automatic programming of numerically controlled machine tools'. Proceedings of the Computer Applications Symposium, Chicago (US), pp. 80–99

60. S.D. ROTH (1980), 'Ray casting as a method for solid modeling'. General Motors Research Laboratories Computer Science Department Research Publication GMR-3466

61. M.A. SABIN (1971), 'An existing system in the aircraft industry. The British Aircraft Corporation Numerical Master Geometry system'. *Proceedings of the Royal Society of London*, Vol. A321, pp. 197–205

62. M.I. SHAMOS (1976), 'Geometric Complexity'. Proceedings of the 7th ACM SIGACT Conference, Albuquerque (US), pp. 224–33

*63. I.E. SUTHERLAND, R.F. SPROULL and R.A. SCHUMACKER (1974), 'A characterisation of ten hidden-surface algorithms'. *ACM Computing Surveys*, Vol. 6, No. 1, pp. 1–55

64. R.B. TILOVE (1977), 'A study of geometric set-membership classification'. University of Rochester Production Automation Project Technical Report TM-30

65. H.B. VOELCKER and A.A.G. REQUICHA (1977), 'Geometric modelling of mechanical parts and processes'. *IEEE Computer Magazine*, Vol. 10, No. 12, pp. 48–57

66. A.F. WALLIS and J.R. WOODWARK (1982), 'Graphical input to a Boolean solid modeller'. Proceedings of the CAD-82 Conference, Brighton (UK), pp. 681–8

67. A.F. WALLIS and J.R. WOODWARK (1984), 'Creating large solid models for NC toolpath verification'. Proceedings of the CAD-84 Conference, Brighton (UK), pp. 455–60

68. A.F. WALLIS and J.R. WOODWARK (1984), 'Interrogating solid models'. Proceedings of the CAD-84 Conference, Brighton (UK), pp. 236–43

69. K.K. WANG and P. KHULLAR (1980), 'Computer-aided design of injection molds using TIPS-1 system'. Proceedings of the CAM-I International Spring Seminar, Denver (US), pp. 35–46

70. J.E. WARNOCK (1969), 'A hidden-surface algorithm for computer-generated halftone pictures'. University of Utah Computer Science Department Report TR4-15

71. M.A. WESLEY, T. LOZANO-PEREZ, L.I. LIEBERMAN,

114   *References*

M.A. LAVIN and D.D. GROSSMAN (1980), 'A geometric modelling system for automated mechanical assembly'. *IBM Journal of Research and Development* Vol. 24, No. 1, pp. 64–74

72. M.A. WESLEY and G. MARKOWSKY (1981), 'Fleshing out projections'. *IBM Journal of Research and Development*, Vol. 25, No. 6, pp. 938–54

*73. P.J. WILLIS (1985), 'A review of recent hidden surface removal techniques'. *Displays*, Vol. 6, No. 1, pp. 11–20

74. T.C. WOO (1977), 'Computer-aided recognition of volumetric designs—CARVD'. In *Advances in Computer-Aided Manufacture*, D. McPherson (ed), North-Holland. (Proceedings of the PROLAMAT 76 Conference, Stirling (UK)), pp. 121–35

75. J.R. WOODWARK and K.M. QUINLAN (1982), 'Reducing the effect of complexity on volume model evaluation'. *Computer-Aided Design*, Vol. 14, No. 2, pp. 89–95

76. B. WORDENWEBER (1984), 'Finite element mesh generation'. *Computer-Aided Design*, Vol. 16, No. 5, pp. 285–91

Index

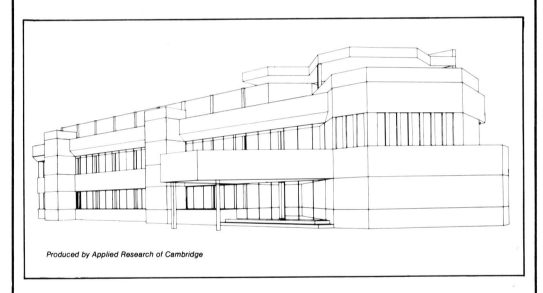